Talking Heads 2

Talking Heads 2

ALAN BENNETT

This book is published to accompany the television series *Talking Heads 2* which was produced by Slow Motion and first broadcast on BBC 2 in 1998.
Executive Producer: Mark Shivas

Commissioning Editor: Vivien Bowler
Project Editor: Martha Caute
Art Director: Ellen Wheeler
Designers: Andrew Barron & Collis Clements Associates

Published by BBC Worldwide Ltd,
Woodlands, 80 Wood Lane, London W12 0TT

First published 1998
© Forelake Limited 1998
The moral right of the author has been asserted

The photograph on page 2 is by Ray Moller © BBC Worldwide 1998;
the photograph on page 22 is by Stephen Morley, on page 90 by Nick Fulton,
the other photographs are by Simon Mein, all © Slow Motion

ISBN 0 563 38460 3

Typeset in Bodoni and Adobe Garamond
Printed and bound in Great Britain by Redwood Books, Trowbridge
Jacket printed by Belmont Press Ltd, Northampton

CONTENTS

INTRODUCTION

These six monologues have been a long time coming: I've been intermittently trying to write them since 1988 when the first series went out. Had I not stopped at six then, I think I could have gone on and written another half dozen without too much trouble, but seeing the first lot produced with a measure of success made the next batch harder to do. I've kept putting them aside and even when they were, in effect, finished I left them in a drawer for a year as I felt they were too gloomy to visit on the public.

This gloom is not deliberate: it is just the way they have turned out. Nor is it that, as I grow older, I take a grimmer view of the world. It's simply that, though I may sit down with the intention of writing something funny, it seldom comes out that way any more. I don't feel called upon to offer any further explanation, though I shall doubtless be asked to account for it, if only by students.

A few years after the televising of the first series of *Talking Heads* they were made part of the A Level syllabus. While I was not unflattered by this it did land me with dozens of letters from candidates wanting a low-down on the text. Some of them, it was plain, thought that writing to the author was a useful way of getting their homework done for them; others were more serious, genuinely feeling that I could give them some clues as to the inner meaning of what I had written. I fell in with very few of these requests, generally sending a postcard saying that their ideas about the monologues were as good as mine and they should treat me like a dead author, who was thus unavailable for comment.

This was not entirely facetious. A playwright is not the best person to talk about his own work for the simple reason that he is often unaware of what he has written. Someone (I think, Tom Stoppard) has compared the playwright confronted by his critics to a passage through Customs. Under the impression he has nothing to declare the playwright heads confidently for the Green exit. Alerted (and irritated) by this air of confidence an official of the Customs and Excise steps forward and asks our writer formally 'Have you any contraband?' 'No,' smiles the playwright. 'Very well,' says the officer, 'kindly open your suitcase.' Happy to comply (he has nothing to be ashamed of, after all) the playwright throws back the lid. Whereupon to his horror there lie revealed a pair of disgustingly dirty underpants and some extremely pungent socks. The playwright is covered in confusion; for though these underpants are undoubtedly his and the socks too, nevertheless he has no recollection of having packed them, still less of giving them pride of place on top of his belongings. The customs officer sniffs (as well he might). However, since there is as yet no law against the import of dirty underpants or smelly socks, the officer gingerly puts them on one side and delves further into the playwright's case.

The next revelation is some photographs. These too take the playwright by surprise. Had he packed them? Surely not. But they are most certainly his: this is a photograph of his father and here are three photographs of his mother and at least half a dozen of himself. 'Rather fond of ourselves, aren't we sir?' murmurs the customs man insolently. The playwright stammers some excuse, only thankful that the snaps are after all quite decent. But his relief is premature because, after sifting through yet more soiled clothing, the customs man now unearths another photograph: it is the playwright again, only this time he has his trousers down, he is smiling and with every appearance of pride he is showing his bottom to the camera. Now not only does the playwright not remember packing this photograph, he doesn't even remember it being taken. But this is him; those are his trousers; that is his smile and, yes, that, without question, is his bottom. 'One of our holiday snaps is it, sir?' sneers the customs officer. 'I should keep that covered up if I were you. We all have one, you know.'

And so the embarrassing examination goes on, the searcher uncovering ever more outrageous items – ideas the playwright thought he had long since discarded, an old marriage, a dead teacher and even a body or two locked in a long forgotten embrace, none of which the playwright ever dreamed of packing but which somehow have found their way into this commodious suitcase, his play.

So there is not much point in my telling you or the A Level students what *Talking Heads* is about or what I have put into my particular suitcase. All I can do is list some of the contents, note some of the themes (or at any rate recurrences), trace the origins of some of these pieces (insofar as I am aware of them) and link them occasionally with other stuff that I've written, always remembering that the relationship between life and art is never as straightforward as the reader or the audience tend to imagine.

That fictional characters are not drawn directly from life is a truism. Evelyn Waugh's epigraph to *Brideshead Revisited* puts it succinctly: 'I am not I; thou are not he or she; they are not they.' But such a straightforward disavowal is misleading, because characters *are* taken from life: it's just that they are seldom yanked out of it quite so unceremoniously as the public imagines. They aren't hi-jacked unchanged into art or shoved just as they are onto the page or in front of the camera: the playwright or novelist has to take them to Costume or Make-up in order to alter their appearance and sometimes he even takes them to a surgeon to change their sex. So that when the writer has finished with them they come on as someone far removed from the character they started off as, yet still, as in dreams, sharing his or her original identity.

And as it is with characters so it is with places. I hope no one ever tries to construct an exact topography of these or any of my other plays because I use street names at random, generally picking out the names I remember from my childhood in Leeds regardless of their geographical location. The posh suburbs then were Lawnswood and Alwoodley, and that still holds good, but otherwise the place I have in my head is only distantly related to Leeds as it is now and as in dreams, again, one landscape adjoins another without logic or possibility. In *Playing Sandwiches*, for instance, Wilfred has been an attendant at the Derby Baths, but of course the Derby Baths aren't in Leeds they're in Blackpool, as I'm sure many viewers will write and tell me. I imagine that in my cavalier (or slipshod) attitude to topography I'm not untypical which leads me to suppose that handbooks to Proust, say, or keys to Dickens, tell only a fraction of the truth.

I note the recurrences, which may indicate preoccupations, though they may equally well betray the poverty of my imagination: there are two dogs, for instance, one a chow with an arthritic hip that gets to run along the Scarborough sands in *Miss Fozzard Finds Her Feet*, the other a noisy alsatian which gets its owner acquitted in *The Outside Dog*. It was only when the monologues were being edited that I realised I had called both dogs Tina, which in *A Woman of No Importance* is also the name of Mr Cresswell and Mr Rudyard's Jack Russell.

Two characters have strokes; two receive counselling; one husband is a murderer, another character is said to be a murderer (by virtue of being a tobacconist); and another husband gets murdered. The murders mystify me, the strokes less so as I am getting to the age when that sort of thing begins to nag, though that isn't really why they figure here. What can or cannot be said is a staple of the drama and it's in this regard rather than attempting an accurate depiction of the condition that I've written about strokes. Or 'cerebral incidents' as neurologists tend to call them nowadays, doctors as inhibited in their own speech as some of the stricken patients whom they are treating.

That Violet's account of the last visit of her sweetheart should be flawless is perhaps a romanticised view of aphasia, owing something to the occasional dispensation from their symptoms enjoyed by Parkinsonian patients rather than stroke victims. Violet's remark that if she could sing everything then she wouldn't forget, is more true of sufferers from Parkinson's than it is of those incapacitated by a stroke, Parkinsonians sometimes being able to dance through a door when they are incapable of walking through it.

The press are several times unkindly noticed though not, I think, unfairly. Having on several occasions had to put up with their intrusions myself, I find I now make no distinction between reporters from the *Daily Mail* or journalists from the *Guardian*: they are more like each other than they are ordinary human beings.

Though neither the *Mail* nor the *Guardian* is a Murdoch paper, Murdoch is certainly to blame for pushing down standards not merely, as Dennis Potter said in his final interview, in journalism but in politics too and other areas of the nation's life. The danger with Mr Murdoch is that he has been around now for long enough to have mellowed into a familiar villain whose unscrupulous behaviour no longer surprises; because he is so routinely self-seeking we have begun to take it with a shrug if not a smile. So it would have been with Hitler had he lived, *Desert Island Discs* the English reward for a long life, however ill-spent.

I note the absence of children. Nearly all these women are childless, only ninety-five-year-old Violet having a son but whom she doesn't recognise as such because, with his 'big wristwatch, attaché case and one of those green raincoaty-things they shoot in', he looks more like a father than a son. No one else has children, not even in Australia where I've sometimes posted inconvenient offspring much as they did in the nineteenth century. I suppose I feel that children blur the picture and mitigate the sadness and, bringing their own problems with them, they demand to be attended to, and want to put their spoke in and are every bit as awkward in the drama as they are in life but with none of the compensations. One thing at a time is my motto and keep children out of it.

There's no sense in Wilfred having a child in *Playing Sandwiches* because the audience would just be waiting for him to interfere with it. Miss Fozzard is unmarried and past child-bearing anyway: I suspect, though, she wouldn't care for children particularly in the context of soft furnishings. Nor would Celia, the owner of the antique shop in *The Hand of God*. With her philosophy of,

> 'Lovely to look at, nice to hold,
> but if you break it I say Sold!'

she wouldn't want small hands picking up her bibelots. I was once in an antique shop which a (not very unruly) child had just left. 'No,' said the woman behind the counter, 'I don't care for children, and that was a particularly bad example of the genre.'

On the other hand a child might have helped both Marjory in *The Outside Dog* and Rosemary in *Nights in the Gardens of Spain*, taking Marjory's mind off housework and Rosemary's off the garden. But it would also have meant there would have been no story to tell.

Another omission is, of course, the television set, which one would expect to be chattering away in the corner of many of these rooms but which must invariably be censored by playwrights protective of their dialogue. These are not naturalistic pieces but even plays that claim to be faithful accounts of ordinary life can seldom accommodate this garrulous intruder. The world of everything that is the case is not the world of drama.

Miss Fozzard Finds Her Feet is my second stab at chiropody, the first being *A Private Function* in 1985. I have no idea why chiropodists should strike such a chord, though when my mother was getting on and I had to sit in on a visit by the local chiropodist the situation did feel quite comic. Bernard's reference to 'your foot feller' is taken from another visit by the same chiropodist: finding my parents out, he left the time of their appointment with a neighbour, who, unable to spell chiropodist, put a note through the door saying, 'Foot Feller, Tuesday 3.30'. Finding the note my father claimed he thought it was a racing tip.

Feet did figure in my childhood as one of my aunties worked in Manfield's shoe shop on Commercial Street in Leeds and when she came round to see us in the evening she would regale us with all the events of her day, told in Proustian detail. When the door eventually closed behind her Dad would burst out, 'I wouldn't care but you're no further on when she's done.'

The names of shoes, the 'fur-lined Gibson bruised look' which Mr Dunderdale has Miss Fozzard try on, comes from twenty years ago when I was filming in an old-fashioned shoe shop in West Hartlepool. Feeling this was what proper writers did I took down a selection of names of shoes from the boxes stacked on the high shelves. I am sure the ankle-hugging bootee in Bengal bronze that Mr Dunderdale gives to Miss Fozzard is not a 'fur-lined Gibson bruised look' and I suppose I could verify this by walking down the road to Camden High Street where, to the detriment of the street as a decent shopping centre, every other shop is a shoe shop. But perhaps not, the expertise of the assistants in

Camden stretching to the knowledge that shoes go on the feet but not much beyond that.

The department store where Miss Fozzard presides over Soft Furnishings is called Matthias Robinson's, which was indeed a department store on Briggate in Leeds and which closed early in the sixties. The name itself is sufficient to stamp it as an old-fashioned emporium of which there were many in Leeds: Wheatley and Whiteley, Marsh Jones and Cribb, Marshall and Snelgrove and in Bradford, memorably, Brown Muff's. Marshall and Snelgrove was a smarter store than Matthias Robinson's but both had the same hushed, carpeted elegance, soft lighting and snooty assistants (like Miss Fozzard) who called my mother 'madam' and so got her all flustered. Near where Matthias Robinson's stood is now Harvey Nichols which aspires, I suppose, to be the smartest store in Leeds though nowhere quite captures the elegance of those grander stores or their seductive smell, a blend of perfume, leather, warm carpet and (in Bradford particularly) fur coats.

When the Sistine Chapel was being restored in the 1980s, anyone with influence in the art world would be taken up in the lift to watch the restorers at work. Thus it was that several people I came across claimed to have reached out and touched either the hand of God or the finger of Adam. Easy-going as the Italians are I would be surprised if these accounts were altogether true but they gave me the idea for the beginning of a film script, *The Hand of God*, which I wrote but never managed to get produced. The script centred round a priceless drawing by Michelangelo of the hand of God wearing the ring of Michelangelo's patron, Julius II, and it's this drawing which (never having made it into a film script) turns up in the box of odds and ends grudgingly given to Celia on the death of Miss Ventriss.

'If you love beautiful things,' says Celia, 'which is why I came into this business in the first place, it breaks your heart.' I detect here a thirty-year-old echo of the only TV comedy series I ever did, *On the Margin*. The first programme featured an antique shop, with myself as the camp proprietor:

DEALER If you don't see what you want you've only got to ask. I don't put everything in the shop window.
CUSTOMER Could I just sort of nose around?
DEALER Feel free. You must excuse my hands but I've just been stripping a tallboy.
[All this seemed quite daring in 1966.]

Mind you I'm not in this business to make money. I'm in this business because I like beautiful things and I like beautiful people to have beautiful things. Which is why I'm very anxious to sell something to you. You see, I believe, perhaps wrongly, that if only all the beautiful people in the world had all the beautiful things there would be No More War. Don't you agree?

There is some irony in the fact that this blueprint for world peace was addressed to the young John Sergeant, who played the Customer but who is now the doyen of the BBC's political correspondents.

Nowadays antique shops are getting thin on the ground, most selling done not through shops but at antique fairs and car boot sales. It's an altogether more knowing business than it was, Sotheby's and Christie's having started the process and shaken down the country in quest of anything saleable. Celia remarks that Sotheby's and Christie's are no better than barrow boys: rather worse, in my view, as barrow boys don't charge a percentage to both buyer and seller and make them feel socially inferior into the bargain. Then there's the *Antiques Road Show* which has set everyone scouring their attics and fetching out their cherished heirlooms. Despite their eagerness to know the value of their precious possessions I have never seen anyone on the programme admit to wanting to sell the objects in question. It's a cosy contribution to our national hypocrisy.

I imagine Celia's shop as bare and uninviting, full of big furniture with not much in it in the way of bric-a-brac, the kind of shop I'd think twice about going into. Such establishments, though, are no longer the norm. Antique shops, as Celia would be the first to point out, have come down in the world. Typical stock nowadays might be a lace doyley; a napkin ring; a Penguin Special from the forties; an empty scent spray from a thirties' dressing table, redolent of long-dead 4711, and an old Oxo tin. Not antiques at all, of course, but 'collectables'.

And collectables that tread hard on the heels of the present so one is nowadays regularly confronted by items classified as antiques which one remembers in common use. Milk was brought round from door to door when I was a boy by Mr Keen the milkman with his horse and cart – and this in suburban Armley. The milk was ladled out of his lidded oval pail in gill measures, both pail and measure now regularly on offer in antique shops, the pewter buffed, the brass polished and both, I suppose, serving ultimately as receptacles for flowers or the ubiquitous pot-pourri. The history of popular taste in the eighties and nineties could be charted via the march of pot-pourri; in the twenties scenting

Ottoline Morrell's lacquered rooms at Garsington, today, as Celia points out, on sale at any garage.

I miss the old-fashioned antique shops: Slee's on the upper floors of premises on Boar Lane in Leeds, where the stock was so shabby and slow-moving it seemed as if it had been aged on the premises; Taylor's in Harrogate which had in its window photographs of that famous magpie, Queen Mary, emerging from the shop in her toque and parasol, with some hapless lady-in-waiting bringing up the rear with the articles Her Majesty had admired and which etiquette demanded she must forthwith be given. Another classy establishment was Frank Williams' in Burford in Oxfordshire where I remember first going forty years ago as an undergraduate and which is now reduced to selling shirts, though at least it doesn't sell the 'pictures of mice in pinnies-type-thing' that Celia groans about (though there's no shortage of that in Burford either). And I know all this is snobbish and strikes the *lacrimae rerum* note; I should leave Celia, though a far from sympathetic character, to voice my regrets and reminiscences for me.

I realise, incidentally, as I write that the finger of God which is Celia's downfall is (and it was entirely unintentional) the finger that singles out the winners of the National Lottery.

Just as in the first series of *Talking Heads* there is only one male monologue and five by women. After that series a viewer wrote to me suggesting that if I wrote a series wholly for men I could call it *Talking Balls*. Which, had I been able to write six male monologues, I would happily have done. That I can't, I put down to the fact that when I was a child the women did most of the talking so that I've been more attuned to the discourse of women than to that of men, and though such real life monologues I come across nowadays are generally in the mouths of men I don't find male talk easy to reproduce; though it's easier when the men are damaged as Wilfred is in *Playing Sandwiches* and Graham in *A Chip in the Sugar*.

Playing Sandwiches dates back twenty years and is linked to a very different play, *The Old Country*, in which the main character, Hilary, is, or has been, a Soviet spy working in the Foreign Office. Accustomed to rendezvous with his Russian opposite number at various locations in London's outer suburbs he recalls how by sheer chance he nearly came to grief:

It's quite hard to be absolutely alone. I never have. Though I have seen it. One particular afternoon I had been on one of my little

jaunts, kept my appointment. Nothing unusual had occurred or was
in the least likely to occur. It was a routine Thursday and I strolled
back to the station across a piece of waste ground that I knew made a
nice short cut. I must have seemed a slightly incongruous figure in
my city clothes. I never dressed the part, even to the extent of an old
raincoat. At which point I came over the brow of the hill and found
myself facing a line of policemen, advancing slowly through the
undergrowth, poking in ditches with long sticks, hunting for
something. It appeared there was a child missing, believed dead.
Clothes had been found; a shoe. It was a bad moment. I had no
reason at all for being there. I was a senior official in the Foreign
Office. What was I doing on a spring afternoon, with documents in
my briefcase, crossing a common where a child had been murdered?
As it was no one thought to ask me any questions at all. I looked too
respectable. And indeed they already had a suspect waiting
handcuffed in the police car. I joined in the search and was with
them when they found the child about half an hour later, lying in a
heap at the foot of a wall. I just got a glimpse of her legs, white, like
mushrooms, before they threw a blanket over her. She had been dead
a week. I saw the man as the police car drew away through lines of
jeering housewives and people cycling home from work. Then they
threw a blanket over him too. The handy blanket. And I have a
feeling he was eventually hanged. Anyway it was in those days.
I came back, replaced the documents, had my tea by the fire in the
Foreign Office. I took in some parliamentary questions for the
minister, had dinner at the Garrick and walked home across the park.
And in a tiled room at Uxbridge Police Station there would have
been that young man waiting. Alone in a cell. Alone in custody.
Alone at large. A man without home or haven. That is what you
have to do to be cast out. Murder children. Nothing else quite
does the trick, because any other crime will always find you friends.
Rape them, kill them and be caught.
(*The Old Country*, pp. 52–3)

The young man has had to wait twenty years for his case to be
considered so he is no longer quite so young or living in the
metropolitan suburbs but two hundred miles north near a municipal
park. But it is the same man.

I am repelled by the self-righteous morality of gaols and their
hierarchy of offences whereby murder and grievous bodily harm are

thought of as respectable crimes and sexual offences are not. I also feel that the press hysteria over paedophilia, and in particular over offences that occurred long in the past, has reached dangerous proportions and the availability of monetary compensation for the possible psychological effects of these injuries has made the situation more fraught with difficulties. But such is the atmosphere surrounding the subject that one thinks twice before setting out any opinions one might have on the matter.

Murder is a messy business and for Marjory in *The Outside Dog* one feels it's just another skirmish in her continuing campaign against dirt. Even a more balanced character like Rosemary in *Nights in the Gardens of Spain* shares some of the same concerns so her first thought in seeing Mr McCorquodale's blood on the sheepskin rug is what a job it's going to be getting it off.

Somewhere Proust says that no matter how sad the occasion with women it will eventually resolve itself into a question of trying on. It could, more charitably, be said to turn into a question of cleaning down, though that's a side of life Proust didn't see much of.

Keeping dirt at bay in the way that Marjory does used to take up a substantial part of every housewife's day: there was the shaking of the rugs, the blackleading of the range, having a run round with the Ewbank, not to mention putting mountains of washing through the wringer. This was the lot of every self-respecting housewife in Leeds in my childhood, where in addition to the soot there was a continuous rain of fine grit from Kirkstall Power Station.

For a woman to adhere to such a routine (and the assumptions behind it) today seems wilful or neurotic, a deliberate narrowing of the scope and satisfactions of her sex. In those days keeping a clean house was the be-all and end-all, every day the occasion for the ceremony of purification, the successive stages of which culminated around the middle of the afternoon with the celebrant sinking into a chair before making the solemn declaration, 'This is the first time I've sat down all day.' There would then be a brief interval before the children came home from school and the men from work and the place was turned upside down again.

I see my mother sitting by the newly blackleaded range, her leg nearest the grate mottled blue-black by the fire as women's legs often were then, and saying imploringly, 'I've just got the place straight. Don't upset.'

This is not the first time I have written about it:

1 May 1978, Hartlepool (Afternoon Off)
We film in the sluice room of the cottage hospital. Racks of stainless-steel bottles and bedpans, a sink that flushes and a hideously stained drum on which the bedpans are sluiced out. This room would be my mother's nightmare. Conditions are cramped and I crouch behind the camera tripod in order to see the action. I am kneeling on the floor under the bedpan sluice. If my Mam saw this she would want to throw away trousers, raincoat, every particle of clothing that might have been touched and polluted. This has got into the film. Thora Hird plays a patient in the hospital being visited by her husband.

'I bet the house is upside down,' she says to him.

'It never is,' says her husband. 'I did the kitchen floor this morning.'

'Which bucket did you use?'

'The red one.'

She is outraged. 'That's the outside bucket. I shall have it all to do again.'

I am assuming this is common ground and that the tortuous boundary between the clean and the dirty is a frontier most households share. It was very marked in ours. My mother maintained an intricate hierarchy of cloths, buckets and dusters, to the Byzantine differentiations of which she alone was privy. Some cloths were dish cloths but not sink cloths; some were for the sink but not for the floor. There were dirty buckets and clean buckets, brushes for indoors, brushes for the flags. One mop had a universal application while another had a unique and terrible purpose and had to be kept outside, hung on the wall. And however rinsed and clean these utensils were they remained tainted by their awful function. Left to himself my Dad would violate these taboos, using the first thing that came to hand to clean the hearth or wash the floor. 'It's all nowt,' he'd mutter, but if Mam was around he knew it saved time and temper to observe her order of things. Latterly, disposable cloths and kitchen rolls tended to blur these ancient distinctions but the basic structure remained, perhaps the firmest part of the framework of her world. When she was ill with depression the order broke down: the house became dirty. Spotless though Dad kept it, she saw it as 'upside down', dust an unstemmable tide and the house's (imagined) squalor a talking point for the neighbours. So that when she came home from the hospital, bright and better, her first comment was always

how clean the house looked. And not merely the house. It was as
if the whole world and her existence in it had been rinsed clean.
(*Writing Home*, pp.277–8)

As a child I had a recurring dream, imperfectly dramatised in my play
Intensive Care, in which my mother and I were sitting in a spotless house
when suddenly the coalman burst through the door and trailed muck
throughout the house. Though the dream owed something to the then
adverts for Walpamur in which a child covered an immaculate wall with
dirty hand prints, looking back I see that this intrusive coalman was
probably my father, which accounts for the fact that, despite my alarm,
my mother took this intrusion quite calmly. I can see that *The Outside
Dog* is another version of this dream; not that that is much help to the
viewer or the reader, though it may be useful fodder for the A Level
candidates.

The Vale of York, where the open prison is located in *Nights in the
Gardens of Spain* and where Rosemary and Mrs McCorquodale go on
some of their jaunts, was just out of biking range when I was a boy and
so seldom visited. Pre-prairified and dotted with ancient villages, duck
ponds and grand country houses, it was a distant sunlit idyll and seemed
to me a foretaste of what life must be like Down South. It was England
as it was written about in children's books, and because I go there
seldom still, it has retained some of this enchantment. Visiting country
churches, which I used to do as a boy, is something I've rediscovered in
middle age so in that sense I identify with Rosemary though not where
gardening is concerned. I am no gardener, never managing to take a long
enough view of things, finding the whole business not unstressful; I see
the battle against weeds (ground elder in particular) as a fight against
evil and one which invariably puts me in a bad temper.

Prison for Mrs McCorquodale is a kind of release just as it was for
Miss Ruddock in *A Lady of Letters* in the first *Talking Heads*. This is a
romanticised view, I'm sure, and having occasionally had to speak in
men's prisons it is not a view I would so glibly advance on their behalf.
I tend to regard women's prisons as women's institutes with bars on the
windows, a prison sentence an ideal opportunity to brush up on the rug-
making or learn French. If it were ever so it is not so now, education and
vocational training in both men's and women's prisons the first victims
of cut-backs.

I was put off writing *Waiting for the Telegram* for a long time because
of the purely practical consideration that Violet would have to be

impossibly old (nearly a hundred) to have had a sweetheart killed in the First War. And, of course, the longer I delayed writing the script the more acute the problem became. Eventually I decided that the time factor didn't really matter: in an old people's home time goes at a trickle anyway, what year it is is not of much consequence, least of all to the residents whose own age is often something of a mystery as it certainly is to Violet.

I see her living as a girl up Tong Road in Leeds, the route traversed by the No.16 tram, the tram Violet feels she should have told Spencer about. It was a neighbourhood close-packed with red brick back-to-backs, including 'The Avenues', a run of eighteen streets named by their number, First Avenue, Second Avenue and so on. This was instanced in some sociological account I read as an example of the soullessness of nineteenth-century slum development but it wasn't quite like that. Each avenue had an atmosphere of its own, some certainly better (more genteel), others rougher or dirtier but far from being components in a featureless urban desert that the bare numbers might suggest.

Tong Road, with Sleights the greengrocers, Burras Peake's the outfitters, Gallons the grocers, and Hustwitt's the sheet music and gramophone shop, has long since gone – all that is left the unchanging black silhouette of St Bartholomew's and, a few streets over, Armley Gaol, twin bulwarks of church and state. Nowadays, with flimsy new houses clustered around the gaol, Tong Road seems bleaker than it ever was and certainly with less character, though doubtless a child brought up there today would be able to discriminate between its seemingly identical streets as effortlessly as we did then.

Some question arose during the rehearsing of the piece about the nature of a vanilla slice. It is, I suppose, a downmarket version of a millefeuille, with confectioner's custard sandwiched between layers of flaky pastry and topped off with white icing. Someone bringing vanilla slices home from the confectioner's, fancies too, and certainly fruit pies, would bear the bag like the priest the host, held high on the flat of the hand lest the fruit leak out or the icing adhere to the paper bag. It's a sight – a rite almost – that I associate with Saturday dinner-time when we would be sent 'on to the end' to McDade's, the confectioner's on the corner of Tong Road and Gilpin Place, to get something 'to finish off with'.

Violet keeps being told she will soon be getting a telegram from the Queen, though whether that custom persists and whether it is a telegram I am not sure, though doubtless I shall be told. Telegraph boys still rode the streets on their high bicycles when I was a boy, in their uniform of blue serge with red piping and a little pill-box hat. The telegram itself came in an orange envelope, smaller than the average letter, the message in capital letters on ticker tape stuck on a half sheet of rather mealy paper.

In our family one did not send telegrams lightly, partly because they were expensive but more because one was fearful of the initial shock when the door opened on the telegraph boy, the immediate assumption always being that he brought bad news. This was a legacy of the First War when telegraph boys were over-employed. Bumping over the setts on their high bicycles, every day they brought news of deaths in the trenches so that a single boy in four years of war might tell the fate of thousands. Seeing him go by women would stand at their doors to see which house he stopped at, this pageboy of death. And the same, presumably, in Germany: *Der Todeskavalier.*

I thought once of writing a TV play about such a boy, who, with men being called up, heard in the autumn of 1914 that 'they were taking on down at the Post Office' and so goes and gets his first job. He becomes a telegraph boy for the two years before he himself is old enough to enlist, thus every day bringing tidings of the fate of others that he knows may one day be his own.

And finally, an apology. How dramatists use (and invariably sanitise) illness for their own purposes is an interesting subject. The illnesses change: a hundred years ago if a character needed to fade away it was with TB or 'consumption'. When fifty years or so ago TB ceased to be incurable it lost its popularity as a dramatic disease to be replaced very often by leukaemia, another condition with which a character could make a slow and dignified exit. That neither disease was as tidy or as well-mannered as dramatists chose to imagine seems insulting to the victims and now I am conscious that I have treated Francis's death in much the same way, deaths from AIDS seldom so quick or so clean as I have made his departure, my only excuse being that it is Violet's story more than his.

The six monologues were each rehearsed for just over a week and generally taped over one day at Twickenham Studios. I am grateful to all the performers, the directors and the production team whose names are separately listed and they will know that it is no reflection on them when I say that at every stage of the production process I never ceased to miss the presence of my long-time producer and friend, Innes Lloyd, who produced the first series of *Talking Heads* and who died in 1991. It is to him these monologues are dedicated.

THE
HAND OF GOD

CELIA EILEEN ATKINS

Producer Mark Shivas *Director* Stuart Burge *Designer* Stuart Walker
Music George Fenton

Celia, a middle-aged woman, sits at the end of a refectory table. There are odd plates on the wall, a grandfather clock: the corner of an antique shop. In the course of the monologue Celia sits in various parts of the shop, often by an oil radiator.

I won't touch pictures. I make it a rule. I've seen too many fingers burned.

Woman comes in this morning starts rooting in her shopping bag saying she has something I might be interested in, been in the attic etcetera etcetera. The usual rigmarole. Hadn't thought anything about it, apparently, until she saw something similar on (and I knew what was coming) that television programme about antiques and that someone on the programme from Christie's...

I said, 'Barrow boys.' She said, 'Come again?' I said, 'Sotheby's, Christie's. Barrow boys. Nicely spoken, lovely suits, finger-nails immaculate. But barrow boys.' She said, 'Well anyway, he said £2000.'

I said, 'Well, he would. He doesn't have to get up at four in the morning and flog his ageing Volvo halfway across England just to sit all day in a freezing marquee and come away with two trivets and an umbrella-stand.' £2000! It was one step up from Highland cattle.

She said, 'It's a genuine oil painting. Look at the work that's gone into it.' I said, 'Madam, if you'll forgive me, could I point you along the street in the direction of A Tisket A Tasket? Basically a café it doubles as a bric-a-brac shop and Yvonne does pictures on the side...' though what I didn't say was that they tend to be mice in pinnies-type thing.

I popped over the road to tell Derek and Cyril. They'd just had a buyer in from Stockholm who'd practically cleared them out. Staffordshire mostly, which is their big thing. Doesn't do anything for me but Derek and Cyril love it; chunky, I suppose. Actually I don't have a particular line. Good cottage furniture sums it up, elm, fruitwood and anything painted. And clocks, of course, when I can get hold of them. Plus pots of the period.

Some things I won't sell. Teddy bears, for instance. Teddy bears are a minefield. I was at a sale in Suffolk and saw a teddy bear actually torn apart between two bidders, one of them a vicar.

These days they're all going in for little sidelines. Eking the job out with jam and little pots of chutney. Woman came in the other day, said, Did I have any chutney? I said 'I shall start doing chutney, madam, when Tesco start doing gateleg tables.' But the garage sells pot-pourri so what do you expect?

I think of Lawrence. 'Christ, old girl, I didn't sink my gratuity in this place to start selling bloody condiments.' He was in bomb disposal which was why to begin with we went in for clocks. Though of course there were clocks then. There was everything then. Furniture. Pottery. Stock no problem. And if one had the eye, which I do, one could pick and choose.

Not any more. Take what you can get. And money, money, money. If you love beautiful things, which is why I came into this business in the first place, it just breaks your heart.

And everybody's an expert now, up to all the tricks of the trade. You'll see something catch their eye and they don't ask about it straightaway; they enquire about something else, pretend they're not interested then it's, 'Oh…incidentally, how much is this little thing?' It's the oldest dodge in the world and they expect you to be taken in by it. Of course they've picked all that up off the television. I won't have one. I said to Nancy Barnard, I refuse to watch. She said, 'Well, we only have it because of Fay.' Fay! They're both glued to it!

Wish I could shift this refectory table. It was a real snip when I got it but I've had it a year now and not a nibble. Lovely top. Elm.

She gives a little smile as someone obviously looks in the window.

Old Miss Ventriss seeing what there is. Took two Crown Derby plates off her once, just as a favour, one of them chipped.

Looking a bit frail. Going on.

Lovely cameo brooch.

FADE.

They talk as if you're not in the room.

Couple just now, looking at the Asiatic Pheasant tureen. '£60!' she said, 'I gave £2.10 for mine.' 'Yes, but when?' I wanted to say, '1955?'

And some of them so careless they practically hurl things to the floor. I've got a notice up now:

> 'Lovely to look at, nice to hold,
> but if you break it
> I say Sold!'

Somebody looking in. Goldfish bowl.

No. You can't see the price, however far you bend. You're going to dislocate your neck and you still won't see it, because I've carefully arranged the ticket so that if you want to see the price you'll have to come into the shop. Which you're not doing.

Even if they could see the price they wouldn't understand it because I've got my little code.

She looks at the ticket on the refectory table, at the end of which she's sitting.

I could take £1300 for this at a pinch. I've had it a year. Too long. Lawrence would be reading me the Riot Act. 'Keep your stock ticking over, old girl. Move it on.' And he did, even if it meant not making much.

'It's like Scrabble, my dear. Start saving up for the big one, the seven letter word, and you're done for. Get your letters down. £5 here. £10 there. Buy for x one week, sell for y the next. That's how you make your money.' Look well in a boardroom. Or one of these loft conversion things. I'd even consider £1150.

I kept wondering about Miss Ventriss. So what with not having seen her for a bit I thought I'd just knock on her door, see how she was.

She lives in one of the double-fronted houses on The Mount, original fanlight over the door and a lovely knocker, hand grasping a ball, which can't be later than 1820 though the house I'd have said was Victorian. But of course it's stucco which can cover a multitude of sins, and once I get inside I realise it's seventeenth century and seemingly never been touched. And I'm right, of course she isn't well, been in bed a fortnight and it's Mabel, the home help who answers the door. Now I know Mabel of old because she's been in from time to time with odd bits of stuff, little things…a silver vinaigrette, a jet brooch, spoons and whatnot, stuff I've found homes for straightaway. They all come from Newcastle, apparently, where her aunt's had to go into a home. Anyway Mabel takes me upstairs to see Miss Ventriss, who tells me she's had all sorts of tests and they still don't know what's wrong. Which probably means they do.

Thin little hand. Like dried leaves. Tragic.

Lovely bedside table with piecrust moulding. District Nurse comes while I'm there, plonks a bottle of medicine straight down on it. Criminal. I help give her some Benger's food only she fetches it straight back.

The spoon's silver and while they're cleaning her up I look at the hallmark. Provincial, Bristol, about 1830.

Same sort that Mabel brought in.

FADE.

I love a nice finish…maple, rosewood, and walnut particularly. What I can't abide is stripped pine. I don't see the point, quite frankly. And they're fanatics about it, some dealers. I mean still. They'll strip everything. Five minutes in the caustic tank and it's one hundred years of loving care down the drain. All the character gone.

I was thinking about this at Miss Ventriss's because there's polish everywhere. Walnut, elm, fruitwood. It's like a jewel box. I've been popping round on a regular basis lately, just to relieve Mabel a bit because the old girl's scarcely conscious now, doesn't know I'm there half the time. I sit by the bed with the clock ticking…carriage clock, tortoiseshell veneer, fluted, about 1750. Made me think of Lawrence. Lovely.

Of course, everywhere you look there's something. It's like houses used to be in the fifties, and most of it museum quality practically. It's from her grandfather, he was a great collector apparently.

I said to Mabel, 'What's going to happen to all this?' She said, Well she didn't think there were any relations. There'd been a niece in Canada but she had a feeling she was in an airline crash.

I couldn't get her to take me round at first. Said she was under strict instructions from the solicitors. I said, 'What solicitors are those?' She said, 'Paterson, Beatty and Brown.' I said, 'Well, there's no problem there because I took a kneehole desk off Mr Paterson and gave him a very good price.'

She was still a bit reluctant so I said, 'Mabel, I can well understand why you have to be careful. It's so easy for little things to go walkabout, particularly with old people. Silver, little brooches, you know the sort of thing.' She went a bit quiet so I said, 'Shall we start with upstairs?'

I couldn't believe it. Every room a treasure trove. Amazing.

When I was going Mabel said, 'I'll try and steer some of it your way if I can.' I said, 'Yes, well there'd be a nice little margin on most of this even running to the two of us. If the worst comes to the worst, of course.' Mabel says 'Yes. Though she seems a bit better today. Kept more of her dinner down anyway. Still, you've only to look at her under that nightdress and there's nothing there.' I said, 'Yes. Where did that nightdress come from?' She said 'Her grandmother, I think. It's all hand done. There's half a dozen of them in the linen cupboard, some of them never worn. Tragic.'

Of course the sharks are beginning to gather. I'm sitting by the bed this afternoon when Derek knocks at the door bearing one of Cyril's wizened egg custards. Mabel didn't let him get his foot round the door only then Nancy Barnard rolls up in her terrible beetroot slacks, says that she and Fay swear by some tincture from the swamps of Paraguay that they'd bought in Chelmsford, should she get her some? I said to Mabel, 'They're so transparent.'

Miss Ventriss is asleep so I have a little look at her bed. It's a country piece. About 1830 I'd have said, painted (which always gets my vote) and in such good condition. The doorbell goes again so while Mabel's downstairs I lift up the mattress and where the paint isn't worn it's as good as new.

I'm just tucking the sheet back when I see her little eyes are open and she's watching me. I think she said, 'Happy?' Only Mabel came in just then.

Of course you can't tell when it gets to this stage, it goes to the brain.

The visitor's the priest, come to anoint her and whatnot, just to be on the safe side, as the doctor says she could go any time. Mabel and I left him to it, just stood respectfully in the background. Had a little embroidered cloth that he covered the chalice with, Arts and Crafts by the look of it and a beautiful thing. Pity it can't be used for something.

Pause.

Of course, when she said 'Happy?', what she probably meant was that *she* was happy.

FADE.

I said to Nancy Barnard, 'Am I a person?' She said, 'Come again, love?' I said, 'Am I a person? Or am I simply a professional bargain hunter?'

Because that was what she was implying. I said, 'I've been coming here as a friend.' She said, 'I know that.' Bright red cardigan, carmine lipstick and, at the funeral, leather trousers. Even Nancy had managed to find a skirt. Niece…she'd never even met Miss Ventriss, went to Canada at the age of six. Mabel had given me to understand she'd died in an airline crash. Turns out what she'd had was a hairline fracture, no crash at all.

And of course she comes in for everything. Which is understandable, except that no sooner does she see the place than she announces that aside from one or two of the choicest pieces which she'd be keeping for herself, she'd be sending the rest to Phillips.

I said, 'Mrs O'Rourke, I'm sure there are several local concerns who'd give you a very good price and you wouldn't be landed with the vendor's commission.' Turns out she's not paying much commission anyway as the stuff is of such good quality she'd come to an arrangement.

It was then she offered me this box of odds and ends from the desk drawer…I'd been very kind to her aunt, she said, and she wanted to give me a bit of something in return.

I said, 'Thank you very much but I don't want to be given anything.' She said, 'That's good because with the solicitors being such sticklers I probably ought to charge you a nominal price anyway then it's all legal and above board. Shall we say £5?' I said, 'I don't sell bric-a-brac.' She said, 'Well, if you give me £5 and it fetches more than that you can give the rest to Oxfam.' I said, 'What do you do in Canada?' She said, 'Public relations.' I said 'Oh' pointedly. 'You must be on holiday then,' gave her £5, took the box and went.

Of course being Canadian she probably thought I was being nice.

I haven't been able to face unpacking the box. In fact, I've only just done it now. Much as I expected. One or two pressed glass ashtrays that I can get £2 or £3 a piece for. A little gunmetal cigarette case and a serviette ring. All of them items for the oddments box. The only thing of any interest at all is a rather smudgy drawing of a finger (I think it's a drawing, it may be a print) but the frame is very distinctive. Quite small but with little doors that open so it looks a bit like an altar, nineteenth century probably.

When I've got a minute I'm going to take the drawing out and put something a bit more conventional in, a flower print or something. Smarten it up a bit. Might fetch £30 or so, you never know.

Pause.

Funny thing to put in a frame, a finger.

FADE.

I think the refectory table's gone. Came in this morning. Only young. Curly hair. Can't have been much more than twenty. I said, Was he looking for anything in particular? He said, Well, he did want a little present for his girlfriend but he was interested in the refectory table. Didn't begin by asking the price, which is always a good sign, just said could I measure it for him?

While I'm rooting about looking for a tape measure he picks up one or two bits and pieces. I'd brought Miss Ventriss's little drawing out thinking I could spend the afternoon taking it out of the frame, and I'd just popped it down on the refectory table where he picks it up, then puts it on one side so's he could look more closely at the table top.

When I'd measured it he got underneath and had a proper look; there was a bit of worm but in a piece that age it would be unusual if there wasn't and anyway we both thought it was dead. So he said, What was the best I could do? I'd given £1100 for it a year ago so I said, 'Well, I can't do much under £1700. Say £1650. It's elm.' He said, 'I know. It's beautiful. If it will fit, it's just what we're looking for.' So I give him my card and he writes down the measurements and he's going to ring back this afternoon.

Just as he's going he picks up the drawing again and says 'What is this?' I said, 'Well, it's a finger, isn't it?' He said, 'Yes. I'm not sure I like that, though it's a nice frame. How much is it?'

I thought, Well, it's an educated voice, I'll take a chance. I said, 'I can't really do it much under £100.' He put it down pretty smartish. I said, 'The frame alone's worth more than that.' He said, 'Yes, it's the frame I'm really interested in.'

I reckoned to look at my book. I said, 'Well, I can do it for £90 and if you're not particular for the drawing I can take it out.' He said, 'No, don't bother, I can do that.' And just then somebody comes in and he writes me out a cheque really quickly. I wrapped it up and said, 'And you'll let me know about the table?' He said, 'What?' I said, 'The table.' He said, 'Oh yes. I'll phone you this afternoon. I think it'll be just right.'

I've just popped along to the bank and put the cheque in and now I'm waiting for him to call. It's funny I'd come down to £90 but he was in such a rush he'd still made it out for £100.

FADE.

I said, No, I wasn't the sort of person who is resentful. I'd made my profit and they had made theirs. Selling on, everybody makes something, that's what the antique business is all about.

They'd posed me outside the shop and this young woman stood by the camera and I had to look at her and not at it.

She said, Would I be asking them to give me an ex gratia payment? I said, I didn't think I would be asking and I was sure they wouldn't be offering. Of course it would be nice if they did. I think I would…in the circumstances.

I'd actually forgotten all about it. It was six months ago at least (apparently they had a lot of tests to do on the paper and whatnot). Then Nancy Barnard comes banging on the window one morning before I'd even opened, holding up a copy of the *Telegraph* and pointing to this photograph on the front page. And there's the young man, and a blow-up of the finger.

Which, so all (or anyway some) of the experts say is by Michelangelo, a study (one of the few apparently) of the hand of God on the Sistine Chapel ceiling.

'I knew I'd seen it before,' Nancy says, 'only it was Fay who pointed it out. Glued to the telly box as usual she said it's like the finger they have at the start of the *South Bank Show*. Such a shame! If you watched the telly you might have known.'

What makes it special apparently is the ring. God doesn't have a ring on his finger on the ceiling, I mean why should he...but the ring on my...on the finger has, very faintly, the arms of the Pope who commissioned it...Julius something or other, who was Michelangelo's patron. Very satirical apparently on Michelangelo's part, though I don't see the joke.

But all of which, needless to say, bumps up the estimated price. Not been sold yet but could fetch anything...£5 million, £10 million... unique.

A finger. That size.

'Poor you,' said Nancy. 'Oh,' I said, 'it happens.' Only when she'd gone I was physically sick.

The young man who bought it, whom I thought looked quite classy, turns out to be some young blood from Christie's. Says in the paper he picked it up in a junk shop. Junk shop.

Of course the person who ought to feel really sick is the niece, Mrs O'Rourke. I don't think she can ever have looked in the box so she'll have had no idea. So I've dropped her a line. Wipe the smile off her face.

Been quite busy. Mostly people just wanting a look. At me, chiefly.

Still, they've bought the odd thing. Sold a couple of lemonade bottles yesterday. Only my stock's low. Can't face going to sales yet. And I've still got this bloody refectory table.

Knee deep in tomatoes so I made some chutney. Frilly top. Italic label. 95p a bottle. Sold three this afternoon.

FADE.

M ISS
FOZZARD FINDS HER FEET

MISS FOZZARD PATRICIA ROUTLEDGE

Producer Mark Shivas *Director* Patrick Garland *Designer* Stuart Walker
Music George Fenton

Nondescript suburban sitting room. In the course of the monologue Miss Fozzard sits on various chairs or stands by the fireplace but the setting is the same throughout.

Bit of a bombshell today. I'm just pegging up my stocking when Mr Suddaby says, 'I'm afraid, Miss Fozzard, this is going to have to be our last encounter.' Apparently this latest burglary has put the tin hat on things and what with Mrs Suddaby's mother finally going into a home and their TV reception always being so poor there's not much to keep them in Leeds so they're making a bolt for it and heading off to Scarborough. Added to which Tina, their chow, has a touch of arthritis so the sands may help and the upshot is they've gone in for a little semi near Peasholme Park.

'But,' Mr Suddaby says, 'none of that is of any consequence. What is important, Miss Fozzard, is what are we going to do about your feet? You've been coming to me for so long I don't like to think of your feet falling into the wrong hands.'

I said, 'Well, Mr Suddaby, I shall count myself very lucky if I find someone as accomplished as yourself and, if I may say so, with your sense of humour.' Because it's very seldom we have a session in which laughter doesn't figure somewhere.

He said, 'Well, Miss Fozzard, chiropody is a small world and I've taken the liberty of making a few phone calls and come up with two possibilities. One is a young lady over in Roundhay, who, I understand is very reasonable.'

'A woman?' I said, 'In chiropody? Isn't that unusual?' 'No,' he said, 'not nowadays. The barriers are coming down in chiropody as in everything else. It's progress Miss Fozzard, the march of, and Cindy Bickerton has her own salon.' I said, 'Cindy? That doesn't inspire confidence. She sounds as if she should be painting nails not cutting them.'

'Well,' he said, 'in that case the alternative might be more up your street. I don't know him personally but Mr Dunderdale has got all the right letters after his name. He's actually retired but he still likes to take on a few selected clients, just to keep his hand in. However he does live out at Lawnswood and unless I'm very much mistaken you're not motorised?' I said, 'No problem. I can just bob on the 17. It's a bus I like. No, if it's all the same to you and the Equal Opportunities Board I'll opt for Mr Dunderdale.' He said, 'I think it's a wise decision. Allow me,' (and he winked) 'Allow me,' he said, 'to shake hands with your feet.'

I've been going to Mr Suddaby for years. I think it's an investment, particularly if you're like me and go in for slim-fitting court shoes (squeeze, squeeze). Mr Suddaby reads me the riot act, of course, but as he says, 'It's a free country, Miss Fozzard. If you want to open the door to a lifetime of hard skin, I can't stop you.' What view this Mr Dunderdale will take remains to be seen.

When I get back Mrs Beevers has her hat and coat on, can't wait to get off. Says Bernard has been propped up in a chair staring at the TV all evening. She helps me get him upstairs and then I sit by the bed and, as per the recovery programme, give him a run-down on my day.

Mr Clarkson-Hall down at the Unit says that when somebody has had a cerebral accident, 'In lay terms, a stroke, Miss Fozzard, we must take care not to treat them like a child. If your brother is going to recover his faculties, dear lady, the more language one can throw at him the better.'

I was just recounting my conversation with Mr Suddaby and how they're decamping to Scarborough when Bernard suddenly throws back his head and yawns.

I rang Mr Clarkson-Hall this morning. He says that's progress.

Pause.

I do miss work.

FADE.

I'm just getting my things on to go up to Mr Dunderdale's this evening, when Bernard has a little accident and manages to broadcast the entire contents of his bladder all the way down the stairs. Mrs Beevers is taking her time coming and it's only when I've got him all cleaned up and sitting on the throne that the doorbell eventually goes. Except even then it's not her, just a couple from church about Rwanda. I said, 'Never mind Rwanda, can we deal with the matter in hand and get a middle-aged gentleman off the lavatory?' So we get him downstairs and manoeuvre him onto his chosen chair five inches from the TV screen.

After they've gone I said, 'You can work the remote; it's about time you remembered how to wipe your own bottom.' Not a flicker. Of course, that's where they have you with a stroke: you never know what goes in and what doesn't.

When Mrs Beevers eventually does roll up she's half an hour late which means I've missed the ten past and have to run all the way up

Dyneley Road so by the time I'm ringing Mr Dunderdale's doorbell I'm all flustered and very conscious that my feet may be perspiring. He said, 'Well if that is what is troubling you, Miss Fozzard, I can straightaway put paid to the problem because I always kick off the proceedings by applying a mild astringent.'

Refined-looking feller, seventy-odd but with a lovely head of hair, one of the double-fronted houses that look over the cricket field. Rests my foot on a large silk handkerchief which I thought was a civilised touch; Mr Suddaby just used to use yesterday's *Evening Post*.

He said, 'Well, Miss Fozzard, I take one look at these and I say to myself here is someone who is on her feet a good deal. Am I right?' I said, 'You are. I'm in charge of the soft furnishing department at Matthias Robinson's, or was until my brother was taken ill. Anything you want in cretonne you know where to come.' He said, 'I might hold you to that but meanwhile could I compliment you on your choice of shoe.' I said, 'Well, as a rule I steer clear of suede because as a shoe it's a bit high maintenance, but sometimes I think the effort with the texturiser pays dividends.' He said, 'I can see we share a philosophy. If I may, I'll just begin by clipping your toenails.'

He said, 'Of course as soon as you walked in I picked you out as a professional woman.' I said, 'How?' He said, 'By your discreet choice of accessories.' I said, 'Well I favour a conservative approach to fashion, peppy but classic if you know what I mean.' He said, 'I do. There's been a verruca here, but it's extinct. Do you know why I chose the profession of chiropody?' I said, 'No.' He said, 'It's so that I could kneel at the feet of thousands of women and my wife would never turn a hair.' I said, 'Oh. Is there a Mrs Dunderdale?' He said, 'There was. She passed over.'

When he'd finished he rubbed in some mentholated oil (Moroccan apparently) and said I'd just feel a mild tingling effect which wasn't unpleasant and said my feet were in tip top condition, the only possible cloud on the horizon a pre-fungal condition between two of my toes that he wanted to keep a watchful eye on.

Had on a lovely cardigan. I said, 'I hope you'll excuse me asking but is that cardigan cashmere?' He said, 'Well spotted, Miss Fozzard. This may be the first time you've seen it but it won't be the last, could I offer you a glass of sweet sherry?'

Churchwarden at St Wilfred's apparently, past president of the Inner Wheel and nicely off by the looks of it, a pillar of the community. When he's at the door he says, 'Next time, if you're very good, I shall initiate you into the mysteries of the metatarsal arch.'

I thought about it on the bus and when I gave Mrs Beevers her money I told her that with my wanting to get back to work she'd no need to come again as I was going to advertise for someone permanent. Bernard's got a bit put by and if this isn't a rainy day I don't know what is.

He was watching TV so I switched it off and took him through my evening as Mr Clarkson-Hall said I should. He looked a bit snotty but I said 'Bernard, nobody ever learned to talk again by watching the snooker.' Told him about Mr Dunderdale and the pre-fungal condition between my toes, his cashmere cardigan and whatnot.

As Mr Clarkson-Hall says, 'Miss Fozzard, it doesn't matter what you say so long as it's language: language is balls coming at you from every angle.' And it's working. I'd got him into bed and was just closing the door when I heard him say his first word. I think it was 'Cow'.

When I rang Mr Clarkson-Hall to tell him he said, 'Why cow?' I said, 'Probably an advert on TV.'

Still he agreed: it's a breakthrough.

FADE.

It was just that bit warmer today so I thought if I went along in my mustard Dannimac I could team it with my ancient peep-toe sandals that haven't had an airing since last summer when I had a little run over to Whitby with Joy Poyser.

Well, Mr Dunderdale couldn't get over them. Said he'd not seen a pair like them in fifteen years and that in the support they gave to the instep plus the unimpeded circulation of air via the toe no more sensible shoe had ever been devised. Made me parade up and down the room in them and would have taken a photograph only he couldn't put his hands on his Polaroid. Anyway I'm taking them along so that we can do it next time.

Wants me to go fortnightly until my *tinea pedis* yields to treatment but he's going to do it for the same fee and now that I'm back at work and we've got Miss Molloy coming in to see to Bernard there's no problem.

She said, 'Call me Mallory.' I said, 'Mallory? What sort of name is that? I wouldn't be able to put a sex to it.' She says, 'Well, I'm Australian.' Strong girl, very capable. And a qualified physiotherapist with a diploma in caring. It's Australian caring but I suppose it'll be the same as ours only minus the bugbear of hypothermia.

Ideally I would have preferred someone older, or someone less young anyway only we weren't exactly inundated with applicants which surprised me because I'd have thought it would have been a nice little sideline for a pensioner, though they'd have to be able-bodied. She chucks Bernard about as if he's two ha-porth of copper. Hails from Hobart, Tasmania, originally; I suppose England offers more scope for caring than the bush. And she and Bernard seem to hit it off, says she likes his sense of humour. I said to Joy Poyser, 'News to me. I didn't know he had one.'

Mind you, it's bearing fruit as movement's certainly coming back, he can hop up and down stairs now, more or less under his own steam. Speech too, because of course with him having company all day he gets the practice.

I was telling the whole saga of the stroke to Mr Dunderdale as he was tackling a patch of hard skin. He said, 'What did Bernard do, Miss Fozzard? I said, ' Not to put too fine a point on it, Mr Dunderdale, he was a murderer. He said, 'Oh. That's unusual.' I said, 'Well, he was a tobacconist which comes to the same thing. Sweets and tobacco, a little kiosk in Headingley.' He said, 'Yes, well sweets and tobacco…it's a lethal combination.' I said, 'He smoked, he was overweight and he certainly liked a drink. Worry is another cause, I know, but as I said to Mr Clarkson-Hall that is something he never did. But now, of course he's paying for it. Only what seems unfair is that I'm paying for it too.'

Mr Dunderdale looked up and he said, 'Yes' (and he had my foot in his hand). He said, 'Yes. If there had been thirteen disciples instead of twelve, the other one would have been you Miss Fozzard'.

Green silk handkerchief this time. Last week it was red.

The words are beginning to come back, though, no doubt about it and when he can't manage a word I get him to do what Mr Clarkson-Hall suggested, namely describe what he means and skirt a path round it. Miss Molloy makes him do it as well and she says one way and another they get along. Bathes him every day, rubs him with baby oil, says that where bedsores are concerned prevention is better than cure.

I still go in on a night and give him all my news. Mr Dunderdale had been saying that it was a pity evolution had taken the turn that it did because if it hadn't we might have found ourselves making as much use of our feet as we do our hands, which in the present economic climate might have been just what's needed to tip the balance.
Miss Molloy said, 'That's interesting,' only Bernard just groans.

Personally I'm surprised she can put up with him but she says that by Australian standards he's a gentleman.

I hear them laughing.

FADE.

Soft Furnishings, we're always a bit slack first thing so I'll generally do a little wander over into Floor Coverings and have a word with Estelle Metcalf. I wish it was Housewares we were next to as that would make it Joy Poyser because Estelle's all right but she's a bit on the young side, big glasses, boy friend's one of these who dress up as cavaliers at the weekend.

I said to her this morning, 'Shiatsu.' She said, 'Come again?' I said, 'Shiatsu, what is it?' She said, 'Is it a tropical fish?' I said, 'No.' She said, 'Is it a mushroom?' I said, 'No.' She said, 'Is it Mr Dunderdale?' I said, 'Why should it be Mr Dunderdale?' She said, 'Because most things are with you these days.' I said, 'I shall ignore that, Estelle. Suffice it to say it's a form of massage involving various pressure points on the body that was invented by the Japanese.' She said, 'That's all very well but it didn't stop them doing Pearl Harbour, did it?' Neville's besieging York on Sunday, trying out his new breastplate. Estelle's going along as an imploring housewife who comes out under a flag of truce.

Just then a customer comes in wanting some seersucker slipovers so we had to cut it short. I don't talk about Mr Dunderdale. And if I do she talks about Oliver Cromwell.

I go weekly now, though Mr Dunderdale won't charge me any more. I was sat on the sofa afterwards while he put away his instruments and he said, 'Good news, Miss Fozzard. We seem to have cracked the *tinea pedis*, not a trace of it left. I think that calls for a sherry refill. Are you in a hurry to get off?' I said, 'No. Why?' He said, 'Well, we still have a little time in hand and I wonder if I might prevail upon you to try on a pair of bootees?' I said, 'Bootees?'

He said, 'Well, I'm using the term loosely. They're technically what we would call a fur-lined Gibson bruised look but bootees is a convenient shorthand. The shade is Bengal bronze.' I said, 'Well, they're a lovely shoe.' He said, 'Yes. Cosy, ankle-hugging they make a beautiful ending to the leg. They're a present, of course.' I said, 'Oh, Mr Dunderdale, I couldn't.' He said, 'Miss Fozzard, please. My contacts in the world of footwear procure me a considerable discount. Besides there is a little something you can do for me in return.' I said, 'Oh?' He said, 'My years in bending over ladies' feet have resulted in an intermittently painful condition of the lower back which, if you are amenable you have it in your power to alleviate.' I said, 'I do, Mr Dunderdale?' He said, 'You do, Miss Fozzard. I'm going to put one cushion on the hearthrug here for my head and the other here for my abdomen and now I'm going to lie down and what I want you to do is to step on my lower back.' I said, 'Should I take the bootees off?' He said, 'No, no. Keep the bootees on, their texture makes them ideal for the purpose. That's it. Steady yourself by holding onto the edge of the mantelpiece if you want.'

Then he said something I couldn't hear because his face was pressed into the carpet. 'What was that, Mr Dunderdale?' 'I said, "Excellent," Miss Fozzard. You may move about a little if you would care to.' I said, 'I'm anxious not to hurt you, Mr Dunderdale.' He said, 'Have no fears on that score, Miss Fozzard. Trample away.' I said, 'I feel like one of those French peasants treading the grapes.' He said, 'Yes. Yes, yes.' I said, 'Do you feel the benefit?' He said, 'Yes, yes, I do. Thank you. If you don't mind, Miss Fozzard I'll just lie here for a little while. Perhaps you could see yourself out.'

So I just left him on the hearthrug.

When I got back Bernard is sitting on the sofa with Miss Molloy, both of them looking a bit red in the face. 'We were just laughing,' Miss Molloy says, 'because Bernard couldn't think of a word.' 'Well,' I said, 'he must learn to skirt round it.' 'Oh, he did that all right,' she said. 'You're an expert at that, aren't you Bernard?' And they both burst out laughing.

Mr Clarkson-Hall's very pleased with him. Says he's never known a recovery so quick. Says he didn't have the privilege of knowing Bernard before but he imagines he's now quite like his old self. I said, 'Yes. He is.'

After Miss Molloy had gone he comes in here while I'm having my hot drink and says he's thinking of opening the kiosk again and that Mallory is going to help him. I said, 'Does Miss Molloy have any experience of sweets and tobacco?' He said, 'No, but she's a fun-loving girl with a welcoming whatever it's called and that's half the battle.'

Note from Mr Dunderdale this morning saying his back is much better and that he was looking forward to seeing me next week.

Estelle suffers in the back department, the legacy from once having had to wield a spare pike at the Battle of Naseby. So I was telling her all about me helping Mr Dunderdale with his, only she wasn't grateful. Just giggles and says, 'Ooh, still waters!'

Floor coverings, they ought to have somebody more mature. She really belongs in Cosmetics.

FADE.

I don't know what's got into people at work. I come in this morning and the commissionaire with the moustache who's on the staff door says, 'Have a good day, my duck.' I said, 'You may only have one arm, Mr Capstick, but that doesn't entitle you to pat me on the bottom. Next thing is I'm invoicing some loose covers in Despatch when one of the work experience youths who can't be more than sixteen gives me a silly wink.

I said to Estelle, 'My Viyella two-piece doesn't normally have this effect.' She said, 'Well they're just wanting to be friendly.' I said, 'Friendly? Estelle, I may not be a feminist (though I did spearhead the provision of pot-pourri in the ladies toilets) but people are not going to pat my bottom with impunity.' Estelle says, 'No. The boot's on the other foot,' and starts giggling. I said to Joy Poyser, 'How ever she manages to interest anyone in serious vinyl flooring I do not understand.'

House dark when I got in. I imagine they're in the sitting room, the pair of them only I call out and there's no sound. So I get my tea and read the *Evening Post*, nice to have the place to myself for a change.

Then I go into the sitting room and there's Bernard sitting there in the dark. I put the light on and he's got the atlas open. I said, 'What are you doing in the dark?' He said, 'Looking up the Maldive Islands.' 'Why,' I said, 'you're not going on holiday?' He said, 'No, I'm not. How can I go on bloody holiday? What with?' And he shoves a bank statement at me.

I've a feeling he's been crying and I'm not sure where to put myself so I go put the kettle on while I look at his statement. There's practically nothing in it, money taken out nearly every day. I said, 'What's this?' He said, 'It's that tart from Hobart.' I said, 'Miss Molloy? But she's a qualified physiotherapist.' He said, 'Yes and she's something else… she's a – what do you call it – female dog.'

I said, 'Did you sign these cheques?' He said, 'Of course I signed them.' I said, 'What were you doing, practising writing?' He said, 'No.'

I said, 'Where is she?' He said, 'The Maldive Islands, where I was going to be.' I said, 'Well we must contact the police. It's fraud is this.' He said, 'No it isn't.' I said, 'What did you think these cheques were for?' He said, 'I knew what they were for. For services rendered. And I don't mean lifting me on and off the what's it called. It's stuff she did for me.' I said, 'What stuff?' He said, 'You know.'

I said, 'Remember what Mr Clarkson-Hall says, Bernard. Trace a path round the word.' He said, 'I don't have to trace a path round the bloody word. I know the word. It's you that doesn't. You don't know bloody nothing.' I said, 'Well one thing is plain. Despite your cerebral accident your capacity for foul language remains unimpaired.' He said, 'You're right. It bloody does.'

I made him some tea. I said, 'She's made a fool of you.' Bernard said, 'You can speak.' I said, 'You mean talk. I know I can speak. The expression is, you can talk. Anyway why?' He said, 'Monkeying about with your foot feller.' I said, 'Mr Dunderdale? What's he got to do with it?' He said, 'Little games and whatnot. He's obviously a...a...' I said, 'A what?' He said, 'A...thing.' I said, 'Skirt a path round the word, Bernard. A what?' He said, Skirt it yourself you stupid...four legs, two horns, where you get milk.' I said, 'Cow. You normally remember that.'

I was telling Joy Poyser about it and she said, 'Well, why did you tell him about the chiropodist?' I said, 'Mr Clarkson-Hall said that I should talk to him, it's part of the therapy.' She said, 'It's not part of the therapy for Estelle Metcalf, is it? You told her. She's not had a stroke.' Apparently she's spread it all over the store.

Anyway I came upstairs, left him crying over the atlas, when suddenly I hear a crash. I said, 'Bernard? Bernard?'

Pause.

'Bernard!'

FADE.

Estelle ventured into Soft Furnishings yesterday, first time for a week. Testing the water, I suppose. Said Neville was taking part in the battle of Marston Moor on Sunday. She's going along as a camp follower but they're short of one or two dishevelled Roundhead matrons and was I interested? I said, 'It's kind of you to offer, Estelle, but I think from now I'd be well advised to keep a low profile.'

People don't like to think you have a proper life, that's what I've decided. Or any more of a life than they know about. Then when they find out they think it's shocking. Else funny. I never thought I had a life. It was always Bernard who had the life.

He's worse this time than the last. Eyes used to follow you then. Not now. Log. Same rigmarole, though. Talk to him. Treat him like a person. Not that he ever treated me like a person. Meanwhile Madam is laid out on the beach in the Maldives. He was on the rug when I found him. Two inches the other way and he'd have hit his head on the fender. Lucky escape.

I'd written to Mr Dunderdale, cancelling any further appointments. I didn't say why, just that with Bernard being poorly again it wasn't practical anyway. Which it wasn't.

So it was back to normal, sitting with Bernard, doing a few little jobs. I'd forgotten how long an evening could be.

Anyway, I was coming away from work one night and a big browny-coloured car draws up beside me, the window comes down and blow me if it isn't Mr Dunderdale.

He said, 'Good evening, Miss Fozzard. Could I tempt you up to Lawnswood? I'd like a little chat.' I said, 'Could we not talk here?' He said, 'Not in the way I'd like. I'm on a double yellow line.' So I get in and he runs me up there and whatever else you can say about him he's a very accomplished driver.

Anyway he sits me down in his study and gives me a glass of sherry and says why did I not want to come and see him any more. Well, I didn't know what to say. I said, 'It isn't as if I don't look forward to my appointments.' He said, 'Well, dear lady, I look forward to them too.' I said, 'But now that I have to get help in for Bernard again I can't afford to pay you.'

He said, 'Well, may I make a suggestion? Why don't we reverse the arrangement?' I said, 'Come again.' He said, 'Do it vice versa. I pay you.' I said, 'Well, it's very unusual.' He said, 'You're a very unusual woman.' I said, 'I am? Why?' He said, 'Because you're a free spirit, Miss Fozzard. You make your own rules.' I said, 'Well, I like to think so.' He said, 'I'm the same. We're two of a kind, you and I, Miss Fozzard. Mavericks. Have you ever had any champagne?' I said, 'No, but I've seen it at the conclusion of motor races.' He said, 'Allow me. To the future?'

It's all very decorous. Quite often he'll make us a hot drink and we'll just sit and turn over the pages of one of his many books on the subject, or converse on matters related. I remarked the other day how I'd read that Imelda Marcos had a lot of shoes. He said, 'She did…and she suffered for it at the bar of world opinion, in my view, Miss Fozzard, unjustly.'

Little envelope on the hall table as I go out, never mentioned, and if there's been anything beyond the call of duty there'll be that little bit extra. Buys me no end of shoes, footwear generally. I keep thinking where's it all going to end but we'll walk that plank when we come to it.

I've never had the knack of making things happen. I thought things happened or they didn't. Which is to say they didn't. Only now they have…sort of.

Bernard gets an attendance allowance now and what with that and the envelopes from Mr Dunderdale I can stay on at work and still have someone in to look after him. Man this time. Mr Albright. Pensioner, so he's glad of a job. Classy little feller, keen on railways and reckons to be instigating Bernard into the mysteries of chess. Though Mr Albright has to play both sides of course.

At one point I said to Mr Dunderdale, 'People might think this rather peculiar particularly in Lawnswood.' He said, 'Well, people would be wrong. We are just enthusiasts, Miss Fozzard, you and I and there's not enough enthusiasm in the world these days. Now if those Wellingtons are comfy I just want you in your own time and as slowly as you like very gently to mark time on my bottom.'

Occasionally he'll have some music on. I said once, 'I suppose that makes this the same as aerobics.' He said, 'If you like.'

It's droll but the only casualty in all this is my feet, because nowadays the actual chiropody gets pushed to one side a bit. If I want an MOT I really have to nail him down.

We're still Mr Dunderdale and Miss Fozzard and I've not said anything to anybody at work. Learned my lesson there.

Anyway, people keep saying how well I look.

Pause.

I suppose there's a word for what I'm doing but…I skirt round it.

FADE.

PLAYING SANDWICHES

WILFRED DAVID HAIG

Producer Mark Shivas *Director* Udayan Prasad *Designer* Stuart Walker
Music George Fenton

A middle-aged man in the basic uniform (donkey jacket, navy blue overalls) of a parks attendant. He sits against the planks of a park shelter, painted but worn and covered with graffiti.

I was in the paper shop this dinnertime getting some licorice allsorts. Man serving me said, 'I wish I was like you.' Shouted out to the woman, 'I wish I was him. Always buying sweets, never gets fat.' I said, 'Yes, I'm lucky. Only I cycle.' She said, 'Yes, I've seen you. You work for the Parks Department.' He said, 'Weren't you a lollipop man once?' I said, 'No.' He said, 'I thought I'd seen you, stood at the crossing.' Racks and racks of magazines. Always men in there, looking.

Janet was dressmaking, doing the twins' christening frocks. I said, 'They put on you, Janet. Before these frocks there's been no word for long enough.' She said, 'Well, whose fault is that?' Apricot satin, little buttons down the front.

Mr Trickett nosing round this afternoon at what he calls 'grassroots level' ordains a blitz on the bushes behind the playground. Privet mostly, all stinking of urine and clogged up with every sort of filth...sheaths; jamrags; a shoe; some tights; sick; dog muck. They come over the wall on a night after The Woodman's turned out, lie down drunk in all that filth and stench and do it. They do it in the playground too, laid down over one end of the slide where the kiddies slide along with their bottoms, then just chuck the evidence down anywhere.

I'm nearly finished when Mr Kumar stops with his barrow and brushes and we walk back to the yard together. He's from Bombay so he takes all this filth in his stride. Born a street sweeper, apparently, what they call an untouchable, though he's very neat, you'd never think it. Going on about getting his wife over from India. Got some decent digs in the Brudenells only a person from Liverpool comes and kicks the door in in the middle of the night. Thinks the English don't like the Indians; says the only Indians the English like are the Gurkhas. The Gurkhas cut people's heads off so that makes them the salt of the earth.

As we're going by the office Mr Parlane calls me in and says he's heard from Wakefield but they still can't trace my records. Foreman, dinner supervisor, lollipop man, I must have left some trace, was I sure I'd got all the digits right? I reeled the number off again and he said, 'Well, I'll try Pontefract, Wilfred, but it's been six months now.'

I went the long way round, pushing the bike. Just one kiddy by herself on the swings. Kiddy black. Mother, white, having a cig, watching.

FADE.

Against anonymous wallpaper; a bedroom, say.

I don't like a cargo of relations; I never have. I wasn't particular to go to the christening only Janet wanted to see what her frocks looked like on and anyway, as she said, who are Barry and Yvonne to look down their nose, their Martin's been had up twice for drunken driving.

Slight hiccup round the font because, since Martin hasn't actually managed to turn up they're short of a godfather. Yvonne wants to go ahead without but the young lad who's in charge says that though he personally is very relaxed about it, the church does tend to insist on there being a full complement of godparents.

We're all standing round looking a bit stumped when little Rosalie, who's seven, pipes up and says, 'Why can't Uncle Wilfred be it, he's my godfather.' Barry straight off clouts her only the priest who doesn't look much more than seventeen and new to the parish says, 'Would Uncle Wilfred be a possible solution?' I don't say anything at all only Yvonne gets in quick, 'No, Wilfred wouldn't be a possible solution because…' and Janet looks at her '…because they're not currently motorised.' The priest lad looks as if he's about to say that wheels aren't part of the job description when Yvonne spots Grandpa Greenwood who's just been out to spend a penny and says, 'He'll do'. The priest says, 'Isn't he a bit on the old side?' Yvonne says, 'No he isn't. He still goes ballroom dancing.' So it ends up being him. I said to Janet, 'At least baby Lorraine won't have any problems with the Military Twostep.'

Afterwards we adjourn to Sherwood Road where Pete and Gloria had laid something on, beer chiefly by the looks of it, one of those dos where the women end up in one room and the men in another. There are kiddies all over the place, though, and what with Pete's alsatian plunging around, sheer bedlam. That's irresponsible in my view, a dog that size when there are kiddies about. One snap and they're scarred for life. A lot of larking about with the children, Barry throwing their two up in the air till they screamed then pretends to throw one to me but doesn't. Ginger tash. Big fingers. Does a bit of decorating now and again, was in a remand home when he was young.

Then Pete starts telling his so-called jokes. 'Now then, which would you rather have, Wilf, a thousand women with one pound or one woman with a thousand pound?' 'Else neither,' says Barry and I saw him wink but I didn't take on. I thought I'd go and help wash up only no sooner were all the women in the kitchen when Janet has to embark on the saga of her womb, how we could have had children only the angle of it was wrong. So Yvonne chips in, 'It's not your angle, love, it's his that matters.' So there's a lot of smutty laughter and I go out and sit on the back step.

Little Rosalie's playing in the yard, throwing her ball against the wall, clapping her hands and lifting her leg to throw the ball under, all that. When she stops she comes and sits on the step and I say, 'I think that deserves a sweet, Rosalie,' and give her a licorice allsort. Suddenly there's a banging in the window and Yvonne bursts through the door and gets hold of the kiddy 'I told you, madam,' starts laying into her, and clawing the sweet out of her mouth. The dog's barking, the kiddy's crying, the old man has an accident and they're all shouting. So anyway we came away.

Janet doesn't say anything. Only when we're at the bus stop she says 'I don't want to have to be flitting again. If you made a decision never to buy any more licorice allsorts it would be a step in the right direction.'

So anyway, I promised.

FADE.

The edge of a bandstand, some wrought iron, but scribbled over and defaced.

Anybody that wants to make a fortune should invent something that'll erase the stuff they write up. There's a plaque on the wall by the fountain:

> This park was opened on July 17 1936 by the
> Rt. Honourable the Earl of Harewood KG. TD.

'So eat shit' some bright spark has sprayed across it, with the result I'm down there all morning with the Brasso and a wire brush.

'Think of it as a labour of love, Mr Paterson,' Parlane said. 'The present one's the music-lover.' 'Who?' 'The Earl of Harewood. Father married the old Princess Royal.' He hangs about for a bit then eventually says, Had I got a minute and he hoped I wouldn't take it amiss but had I been in prison? I said, 'No. What would I have been in prison for?' He said, He'd no idea, it was just that when records go walkabout as mine plainly had that was often the case.

I said, Well, it's not the case in this case, thank you very much and

was my work unsatisfactory? He said, 'Far from it, the place has never been so tidy. You, Mr Paterson are a textbook example of why we went performance related. But you're also an example of somebody who has eluded all the fielders and ended up in the long grass, bureaucratically speaking. Well, don't worry. Gordon Parlane is going to make it his personal mission to retrieve you.'

It started spitting this afternoon so I thought I'd keep out of the rain and sweep up the bandstand. Young woman there again, the kiddy; I've seen them once or twice now, poor-looking, eating chips out of a carton.

She says, 'Are we all right sitting here?' I said, 'That's what it's for, visitors.' She said, 'We often come. The council's put us in bed and breakfast only the hotel's got proper people too and they don't like us around during the day. Samantha hates it, don't you Samantha?' The kiddy comes over and offers me a chip. 'You're privileged,' the mother says, 'she's frightened of men generally. Won't go near her father. Mind you, neither will I.'

Bonny little thing, only her mother's put her some earrings in, stud things. And one in her little nose and she can't be more than seven. I wonder the law lets them do it, because that's interference in my view, ornamenting your kiddies, hanging stuff on them as if they were Christmas trees.

I'm sweeping up the rubbish and pretend to sweep up the kiddy too so she starts screaming with laughter. 'Oh,' her mother says, 'I think you've clicked. What is this place?' I said, 'What place?' 'This. This shelter thing.' I said, 'It's a bandstand. The band used to play here once upon a time.' She said, 'What band? You mean like a group?'

The kiddy came and stood by my knee. 'Yes,' I said. She said, 'Where did the fans go then? In the bushes?' She laughed and the kiddy laughed and put her hand on my leg. I said, 'It's stopped raining, I'd better get on.' She threw the chip carton down. She said, 'We'll see you. Wave to the man, Samantha. Wave.'

As I'm pushing the barrow back there's a policeman hanging about the fountain. Said he was just showing the flag and he'd be obliged if I'd keep my eye open for any undesirable elements. I said, 'Drugs, you mean?'

He said, 'Drugs or whatever. Men sitting too long on the benches type thing. Parks make for crime. This beat's a bugger.' As he was going he said, 'Pardon my asking but didn't you use to work at the Derby Baths?' I said, 'No, why?' He said, 'Nothing, the face is familiar. My two both got their bronze medal there. Well, I won't detain you, particularly since our Asian friend appears to be waiting.'

Pushing his barrow back Mr Kumar's all smiles because his wife has arrived. 'They took all her clothes off at the airport but otherwise,' he says, 'it was all as easy as falling off a log. I am a very happy man.'

'They're sly,' Janet said. 'Probably wants your job.' I said, 'What for?' 'His brother, his uncle, his nephew. They're all the same. Anyway I got my promotion. Same grade now as I was before. Keep this up a bit longer, Wilfred, and we might be able to run to a car again soon.'

FADE.

Planks again or municipal bricks. An outside wall, say.

Bit of excitement this morning. Body in the bushes. Little lad found it looking for his ball. Old man, one of the winos probably. Two police cars, an ambulance and more fuss made of him dead than there ever

was alive. The child not worried at all, the mother hysterical. All over
by half past ten and we were soon back in go mode, drizzle included.

I was heading for the tennis courts, trying to steer clear of the
bandstand only Trickett shouts after me, 'Paterson. I don't want you
skulking back there. The bandstand's in a disgusting state.'

Somebody'd thrown up all over the seat and I'd just about got it
cleared up when the girl's calling out and the kiddy comes running in
waving her little pink plastic handbag thing. 'Samantha's got you a
present, haven't you Samantha. Give it to Mr…what's your name?'
The child was putting her arms out to be lifted up.

'Hargreaves,' I said. 'My name's Hargreaves.' 'Give it to him
Samantha,' and she takes out a daffodil from her little handbag and
we put it in my buttonhole. 'She picked it herself,' the mother said.
'My name's Debbie.'

They sit watching while I go on cleaning up. She said, 'You're a bit
too nice for this job aren't you? You look as if you should be doing
something more up-market, a traffic warden or something.'

I said I liked being outside. The kiddy was pretending to help me
sweep up again. 'It didn't used to be like this,' I said, 'all scribbled over
and stuff written up.' 'Oh,' she says, 'I like the lived in look. Cans and
litter and all that. You don't want it too clinical. Anyway it's all litter
basically isn't it…Leaves is litter. Soil. We like it, don't we Samantha?'

I said, 'Why did you put them earring things in?' She said 'Her
studs? Well, I don't see why she shouldn't have all the advantages other
kids have. She's as good as anybody else. Don't you like them?' I said,
'No, Debbie. I do like them.'

After a bit the mother says Did I like her. I said why? She said, 'Well
we keep running into one another.' I said, 'You won't have Samantha
tattooed, will you?' 'Oh no,' she said, 'not until she's old enough to
make her own decisions. It's part of her life choices isn't it? Did the
fountain used to go?' I said, 'Yes. When I was a boy. The fountain went.
The band played. People kept off the grass. It was lovely.'

Mr Kumar comes by and says I have to call in at the office when it's
convenient. He smiles at the girl but she doesn't take on. 'I don't care for
Asians,' she said when he's gone. 'Neither one thing nor the other in my
opinion.'

I went along to the office straightaway only it turns out to be
nothing. Parlane has got some new idea about chasing me up on the
computer. He said, 'I'm going to fax all your details over to Thorpe
Arch, tell them Wakefield has been playing silly buggers (which they're

always happy to hear) and get them as a personal favour to me to beam you up nationally. And if that doesn't work even Gordon Parlane is going to have to admit defeat.'

Coming out I ran into Mr Trickett. 'Oh,' he said spotting my buttonhole, 'Picking flowers now, Paterson?' I said somebody'd broken it off. He said, 'I don't know why we bother. They don't want gardens, they want their hands chopping off. I'd decapitate them let alone the bloody daffodils.' 'Anyway,' he said, 'Get rid of it. It sends the wrong message.'

They were still hanging about when I went back. 'Mr Hargreaves has lost his buttonhole,' Debbie said and the kiddy starts crying only when I pick her up she stops.

On the way home I called in at the sweetshop.

FADE.

Some sort of institutional background, half green, half cream. Wilfred is unshaven, with no tie on.

Janet's just been down apparently. Left a clean vest and stuff at the desk. They said she wasn't allowed to speak to me at this stage; she said she didn't want to anyway.

It was the rain that did it because I'd given the bandstand a wide berth all week only Trickett comes into the yard this morning saying it was all flooded and wasn't that typical, one drop of rain and the place grinds to a halt. Tells me to get some rods and try and locate the problem. So I trundle over there and it's one of the grates that's stopped up. And I'm just getting my arm down to feel what the stoppage was when Samantha comes running along by the railings and puts her little face through the bars.

I said, 'Hello. Are you in prison?' She said, 'No. I've got an umbrella.' And she shows me her baby umbrella.

Her mother's all cross, pulls her away from the puddle and says, 'Are you going to be here long? I've got to go and see my social worker woman. Can I leave her with you for half an hour? She likes you. She won't be any bother.' I said, 'Why can't she go with you?' She said, 'Because her dad'll be there and if he sees her he'll want to keep her. Go on.'

I was going to say no, only I didn't have to because just then Mr Parlane appears and wants a word so they clear off, leaving me with my arm still down the drain. I suddenly feel the culprit and it's two or three

condoms all mixed up with leaves plugging up the pipe so I pull the lot out and all the dammed up water just empties away.

'Success,' I say to Mr Parlane and show him the bundle, 'Problem solved.' He said, 'No, not entirely. Would you step along to the office for a minute or two. And bring your barrow.'

It was Trickett who gave me my cards, with one week's pay in lieu, said I'd made several false statements so I'd better not have any silly ideas about wrongful dismissal and had I thought about bringing the Parks Department into disrepute let alone anything else.

Parlane hung about outside and when I came out said what about working in an old people's home or even a mortuary, somewhere out of harm's way, where I couldn't do any damage. 'Because you're a good worker, Wilfred, you really are.'

I went out the playground way, empty with it being wet, just a woman and a baby. I think she's a child minder. Only suddenly Samantha comes running out from behind the see-saw and gets hold of my hand. I said, 'Where's her mother?' The woman said, 'Gone over to the social. She said she'd be back by now. I've got to go, can I leave her with you?' I said, 'No.' 'Debbie said I could. She'll be back any minute. Let her go on the slide. She likes the slide.'

She wouldn't go on the slide because it was all wet, so we went and sat in the shelter. I put my hand on my knee and she put hers on top of it, then I put mine on and she topped it off with her hand. And we played that game for a bit. Sandwiches she called it.

Then I pretended to go to sleep, only she got on the seat and tried to open my eyes with her little fingers. She kept wanting to hold my hand but I wouldn't. Her little hand kept pecking at my hand, like a little bird trying to get in. Only my hand was a fist, honestly. Tight, she couldn't get in.

'There's nothing in there for you,' I said, 'I don't have anything for little girls. My shop's closed.' 'No it's not,' she says and slips her little finger in between my fingers and wiggles it about and looks at me and laughs.

She laughs again. She knew what she was doing. She must have known what she was doing.

So I took her in the bushes.

FADE.

White tiles. Wilfred is in prison clothes; eye swollen; bandage on his hand.

I said, 'She wanted to show me her dance.' Her mother said, 'What dance? She doesn't have a dance.' Somebody shouts out, 'You'll dance.'

They fetched me in and out the back way under a blanket. Women there shouting. Something hit me on the head. Said in the van it was a packet of cornflakes. Coins as well. Aught they have in their shopping bags.

They have to ravel it all out in words. 'Then what did you do? Then what?' As if there was a plan. As if I meant to go from A to B. 'Well,' says the counsel, 'you bought the sweets, didn't you? You gave the wrong name.' I said to the young policewoman, 'It's what I thought she wanted.' 'That's what men always say,' she said, 'choose how old you are.'

Perhaps it would be easier, said the judge, if Samantha came up here. So she went and stood by his knee and held his hand. I thought, 'Well, that's what I'm here for.'

I asked for a number of other offences to be taken into consideration, some of them in Huddersfield where I've never even been. The police said it didn't matter as it meant they could close the book on lots of cases and it would go in my favour. It didn't. They just said my record proved that I was a hopeless case.

The judge said I would be given treatment. I haven't been given any treatment. They've put me by myself to stop the others giving me the treatment. The getting scalded in the kitchen treatment. The piss in your porridge treatment.

The doctor said, 'Did anyone touch you when you were little?' I said I didn't want any of that stuff. 'No, they didn't. And if they did, it's done. Anyway, they tell you to touch people now. They run courses in it.' 'Not like that,' he said.

Janet's been. Usual tack. Blames the mothers, says if they can't look after them they don't deserve kiddies in the first place. All her daffodils have been rooted up, plant pots broken. Next stop Newcastle, probably.

Mr Kumar. Says, I miss you Mr Paterson. I miss our walks with our barrows and brushes. You are the untouchable now. And he pats my hand. Says he's gone up one rung on the ladder now, is an attendant at the Art Gallery. 'No condoms to speak of,' he says. 'No sick on the floor. And on the walls the beautiful ladies and landscapes of Leeds. I tell you, Mr Paterson, it is a cushy number.'

When they put me away last time I used to think when I got out I'd go somewhere right away, a shed in the middle of a moor. And I'd fence it round with railway sleepers and get myself a bad dog and be a recluse.

Only kids would come. They'd know.

The prison must be near the station. I hear the trains on a night. And a school somewhere. There's a playtime at a quarter to eleven. And they come out at four. It's the one bit of my life that feels right and it's that bit that's wrong.

Men groan and cry out. Shout and scream in the night. It's like a tropical forest. Wild beasts.

I didn't foist them off like grown-ups do. I looked at them. I listened to them.

Sometimes there's a plane crosses the top left hand corner of my window. I think of the 'No Smoking' sign going on, the seats put back in the upright position, the pilot beginning his descent to Leeds and Bradford airport.

I used to go hiking when I was a boy. Over Nidderdale Moors. A reservoir. That would be the place. Nobody there at all.

FADE, and in the black a long drawn-out howl.

THE OUTSIDE DOG

MARJORY JULIE WALTERS

Producer Mark Shivas *Director* Gavin Millar *Designer* Stuart Walker
Music George Fenton

Afternoon. The kitchen. Against a blank, wallpapered wall. One chair. Possibly some artificial flowers. Similar settings throughout.

I'd be the same if it was a cat. Because they make as much mess as dogs. Only cats you can be allergic to, so people make allowances. And flowers, of course, some people. Only we don't have flowers. Well, we do but they're all washable. I just think it spies on me, that tongue lolling out.

He took the van over to Rawdon last night. Said it was Rawdon anyway. Doing something or other, fly-tipping probably. Takes Tina which was a relief from the woof-woofing plus it gave me a chance to swill.

I'd had Mrs Catchpole opposite banging on the door in the afternoon saying she was going to the council because it wanted putting down. I said, 'I agree.' She said, 'I'm getting a petition up.' I said, 'Well, when you do, fetch it across because I'll be the first signatory.' I hate the flaming dog. Of course she doesn't do it with him. Never makes a muff when he's around.

He comes in after midnight, puts his clothes in the washer. I said to him last week, 'Why don't you do your washing at a cultivated hour?' He said, 'You're lucky I do it at all.' Still, at least the washer's in the shed. I shouted down, 'That dog's not inside is she?' He said, 'No. Get to sleep.' Which I was doing only when he comes up he has nothing on. He leaves it a bit then slides over to my side and starts carrying on.

Found a dog hair or two on the carpet this morning so that meant another shampooing job. I only did it last week. This shampoo's got air-freshener in, plus a disinfectant apparently.

Non-stop down at the yard since they started killing off the cows, so when he comes in this dinner-time he wants to eat straight off. Swills his boots under the outside tap and he's coming in like that. I said, 'Stuart. You know the rules. Take them off.' He said, 'There's no time.' So I said, 'Well, if there's not time you'll have it on the step.' Sits there eating and feeding Tina. She licks his boots. Literally. I suppose it's with him coming straight from the slaughterhouse.

Seems to have lost another anorak, this one fur-lined.

FADE.

She comes up this afternoon, his mother, all dolled up. Says, 'You've got this place nice. How do you manage with our Stuart?' I said, 'I've got him trained.' She said 'He's not trained when he comes down our house.' 'Well,' I said, 'perhaps he doesn't get the encouragement.' She said, 'I don't like it when they're too tidy. It's not natural.'

Not natural at their house. They've no culture at all. First time I went down there they were having their dinner and there was a pan stuck on the table. When it comes to evolution they're scarcely above pig-sty level. And she must be sixty, still dyes her hair, fag in her mouth, big ear-rings. She said, 'You don't mind if I smoke? Or do you want me to sit on the step?'

I gave her a saucer only it didn't do much good, ash all over the shop. She does it on purpose. It had gone five, she said, 'Where is he?' I said, 'Where he generally is at this time of day: slitting some defenceless creature's throat. They're on overtime.'

She went before it got dark. Said she was nervous what with this feller on the loose. Made a fuss of Tina. Remembered her when she was a puppy running round their house. I remember it an' all. Doing its business all up and down, the place stank. It was me that trained Stuart. Me that trained the dog.

Except for the din. Can't train that. Leaves off, of course when he appears. He doesn't believe she does it. I said to him, 'Is it safe for me to go on to the library?' He said, 'Why?' I said, 'There's a lass dead in Wakefield now.' He said, 'You don't cross any waste ground. Take Tina.'

Anyway I didn't go and when he's changed out of his muck and swilled everything off he put on his navy shirt, little chain round his neck and the tan slacks we bought him in Marbella. I brought him a beer in a glass while I had a sherry. Him sat on one side of the fire, me on the other, watching TV with the sound down. I said, 'This is a nice civilised evening.'

Except of course madam gets wind of the fact that we're having a nice time and starts whimpering and whatnot and jumping up outside the window and carries on and carries on until he has to take her out. Gone two hours so I was in bed when he got back.

Comes upstairs without his trousers on. I said, 'What've you done with your slacks?' He said, 'The dog jumped up and got mud on. Anyway it's quite handy isn't it?' I said, 'Why?' He said, 'Why do you think? Move up.'

Lots of shouting and whatnot. I thought in the middle of it, it's a blessing we're detached. 'Sorry about that,' he said when he'd done. 'I get carried away.'

Loudspeaker van came round this afternoon saying the police were going to be coming round. House to house. I was just getting some stuff ready to take to the dry cleaners while it was light still.

Couldn't find his slacks.

FADE.

She said, 'Have you any suspicions of anyone in your family?' I said, 'What family? There's only me and him.' He said, 'We can't talk with this dog carrying on. Can't we come inside?' I said, 'You've told people not to open their doors.' She said, 'But we're the police.' I said, 'Well, take your shoes off.'

She's in uniform, he's got a raincoat on. She said, 'We've had complaints about the dog. It's in your print-out.' I said, 'Oh it's the dog, is it? I thought it was the killer you were after.' She said, 'Your hubby says it never barks.' I said, 'When did you talk to him?' She said, 'At his place of employment. These are the dates of the murders. Look at them and tell me whether you can remember where your husband was on any of these dates.' I said, 'He was at home. He's always at home.' She said, 'Our information is he'll sometimes go out.' I said, 'Yes. With the dog. Do you know dogs? They occasionally want to have a jimmy riddle.' She said, 'What about this fly-tipping? His van's been seen.' I said, 'The van's not my province. Though I've shared the back seat with a beast head before now.'

Meanwhile the one in the raincoat's been sitting there saying nothing, looking round, sizing the place up. Suddenly he stands up. 'Can I use the toilet?' I said, 'Now? Well, you'll have to wait while I put a paper down.'

I took him upstairs and waited outside. He says, 'I can't do it with you listening.' So I came downstairs again. And she says, 'He's got a funny bladder.'

'One last question. Have you noticed anything out of the ordinary about your husband stroke boy friend stroke father stroke son...well, that's husband in your case...over the last six months?' 'Like what?' 'Blood on his clothes?' I said, 'There's always blood. He's a slaughterman. Only you won't find any in here. And you won't find any outside. He swills it off.' I said, 'Your friend's taking his time.' She said, 'Men have problems with their water. I've an idea he has an appliance.'

When eventually he comes down he says, 'You keep the place tidy.' I said, 'I used to be a teacher.' He said, 'What did you teach?' I said, 'Children.' He said, 'Do you have any?' I said, 'Does it look like it?'

As they're going Mother Catchpole opposite is stood in the road and shouts across, 'I've got something to tell you.' So the girl goes over and has a word. Comes back. 'Nothing,' she says. 'Just the flaming dog.' 'Nobody listens to me,' she's shouting, 'I've had a depression with that dog.'

I shut the door. When I went upstairs to wipe round the toilet I saw he'd moved one or two ornaments. Nothing else that I could see.

When his lordship came in I said, 'You never told me they'd been to your work.' He said, 'It was routine. I've tipped on one of the sites where they found one of them.' I said, 'Did you find that ticket?' He said, 'What ticket?' 'For the dry cleaners. The tan slacks.' He said, 'Oh yes. They're at work.' I said, 'You're not wearing them for work. They're good slacks are them.' He said, 'They're shit-coloured. What do I want with shit-coloured trousers?'

He was in the yard swilling his boots when he was saying all this. Outside. He's started being much more careful about all that. I don't know what's got into him.

FADE.

Lad opposite just delivering four pizzas to No. 17. She's a widow, living on her own with a son in New Zealand and a heart condition, what's she wanting with four pizzas? I bet she's never had a pizza in her life. They must think I'm stupid. The doctor said, 'Why can't you sleep?' I said, 'The police are bugging my home.' She said, 'Yes. There's a lot of it about.' Asian too. They're normally a bit more civil.

We went out in the van the other night and he stopped it somewhere and said, 'Do you think it's me?' I said, 'No.' He said, 'Well, my mam does. It was her that went to the police.' 'And what did they say?' 'Told her she wasn't the only one. Mothers queuing up apparently.' I said, 'Well, she might cut a bit more ice if she didn't wear that leopard-skin coat thing. Legacy from when she was at it herself.' 'At what?' 'Soliciting.' He said, 'Who told you that?' I said, 'You did. You said she was hard up.' He said, 'It was years ago. I was still at school.'

Went out with Tina later on and comes in all worked up again. Sets to. Thought he was going to go through the bed. And saying stuff out loud again. I thought of them across the road, listening, so I put my hand over his mouth at one point, which he seemed to like.

I waited to see if there was anything in the papers only there wasn't. Been nothing for about a week now. You can get things out of proportion, I think.

I found where they'd put their listening thing this morning. Little hole in the skirting board. Did it when he was reckoning to go to the lavatory. Must have been quick because he'd managed to colour it white so it didn't show only some fluff got stuck to the paint so that's how I spotted it.

Sound of a newspaper coming through the door. She picks it up.

They've found another one, it looks like. This time on a skip. Been there...about a week.

FADE.

One of them leaps over the wall, quite unnecessarily in my opinion because the gate's wide open. They get it off the TV. Five police cars. Batter on the door and when he opens it bowl him over and put handcuffs on him and take him off with a jacket over his head.

Tina, of course is going mad and they've got a dog of their own which doesn't help. I said, 'You're not fetching that thing in here.' He said, 'We've got a warrant.' I said, 'His dog's not been in here so I don't see why your dog should.' He said, 'This is an instrument of law enforcement.' I said, 'Yes, and it's an instrument of urinating against lampposts and leaving parcels on pavements. I don't want it sniffing round my stuff.' He says, 'You've got no choice, love,' and shoves me out of the way.

One of them's upstairs going through the airing cupboard. I said, 'What are you looking for? Maybe I can help?' He said, 'If you must know we're looking for the murder weapon.' I said, 'Oh, I can show you that. This is the murder weapon *(Points to her tongue)*. This is always the murder weapon. You want to drag the canal for that.'

He said, 'You sound sicker than he does. I don't think you realise the seriousness of your situation. If we find you know what's been going on you'll be in the dock yourself.' I said, 'Don't put those sheets back. I shall have them all to wash now you've been handling them.' He said, 'We shall want all his clothes and other selected items,' and produces a roll of bin bags. 'Is everything here? He hasn't got anything at the dry cleaners?' I said, 'No.' I said, 'How do I know we'll get all this stuff back?' He said, 'That's the least of your worries.'

When eventually they go the handler reckons to take charge of Tina, except that he can't get her to go in the car with them. Then when they do force her in they all pile out sharpish because she's straightaway done her business in the car. I laughed.

It was suddenly quiet when they'd gone, just Mother Catchpole at her gate shouting. 'The doctor says I'm clinically depressed. That dog wants putting down.'

The police said not to touch anything but I wasn't having the place left upset like that so I set to and cleaned down and repaired the ravages a bit. One or two folks outside the house looking in and the phone rings now and again but I don't answer.

Dark by the time I'd finished but I didn't turn the lights on, just sat there. They must have charged him around six because suddenly there's cars drawing up and the phone's going like mad and reporters banging on the door and shouting through the letter-box and whatnot.

I just sit there in the dark and don't take on.

FADE.

Another parcel of excrement through the letter-box this morning. Postmarked Selby. Pleasant place. We had a little run there once in the van. Saw the cathedral, abbey, whatever it is. Shop with booklets and teatowels the way they do. Had a cup of coffee at a café down a street. The postman whanged it through that hard it split on the doormat.

It's probably deliberate. I'd got some plastic down from the previous times but still I'd to set to again. Spend a fortune on Dettol.

The trial's in Manchester for some reason. Out of the area. They can't call me unless I choose. Which I don't. Woman spat at me in Sainsbury's so I shop at the Asian shops now. Everywhere else they stare. Have to go thirty miles to get a perm. Go by minicab. Asians again. Never liked them much before. Don't ask questions. Godsend.

Reporter comes ringing the doorbell this afternoon. I think they must take it in turns. Shouts through the letter-box. I said, 'You want to be careful with that letter-box. You don't know what's been through it.' Says I'm sitting on a gold mine. Talks about £10,000. My side of the story.

Final speeches today. It rests on the dog, apparently, the rest is circumstantial. The van seen where the murders were, stopped once even but nothing else. Nothing on his tools. Nothing on his clothes. Only they found some blood belonging to the last one on the dog. The defence says it could have rolled in the blood because with the dog being fastened up all day when they went off he let it roam all over. So it doesn't mean he was with her, or anywhere near as the dog was off the lead.

The judge likes dogs. Has a dog of his own apparently. I don't know that'll make any difference.

I saw him before the trial started. Looked thinner. I was disappointed not to see him wearing a tie. I thought a tie would have made a good impression only they use them to commit suicide apparently.

I wish I'd something to do. I've cleaned down twice already. The yard wants doing only I can't do it with folks and reporters hanging about.

Pause.

He's lying, of course. Our Tina hasn't been seen to, so when he takes her out he never lets her off the lead. Ever.

FADE.

'Marjory! Marjory!'
They still shout over the gate now and again, one of them there this

morning. Most of them have gone only they leave a couple of young ones here just in case I go shopping. Jury's been out two days now and they think it might be a week.

Anyway I thought while the heat was off I might be able to sneak out into the yard and give the kennel a good going over. The forensics took away her blanket so that's a blessing. I said to the feller, 'Don't bother to fetch it back. I'd have wuthered it long since if he'd let me.'

I peeped out of the gate to see if it's safe to swill and there's just a couple of the young reporters sat on Mrs C's doorstep having a cup of tea. I don't know what she's going to do when it's all over. She's had the time of her life.

Anyway I chucked a bucket of water under the kennel and then another only it didn't seem to be coming out the other side. I thought it was muck that had built up or something so I went in and got a wire coat hanger and started scraping about underneath and there's something there.

It was his tan slacks, all mucky and plastered up with something. I sneaked in and got a bin bag and fetched them inside.

Thinking back the police had been round with the dog but I suppose it couldn't smell anything except Tina. I sit there staring at this bag wondering whether there's anybody I should ring up. Suddenly there's a banging at the door and a voice through the letter-box.

'Marjory! Marjory!'

I didn't listen I ran with the bag and put it in the cupboard under the stairs. More clattering at the door.

'Marjory! Marjory! They've come back, the jury. He's been acquitted. He's got off. Can we have a picture?'

FADE.

The young woman says, 'Did I want any assistance with costume or styling? There'll be a lot of photographers.' I said, 'What's the matter with what I've got on?' She said, 'I could arrange for someone to come round and give you a shampoo and set.' I said, 'Yes, I could arrange for someone to come round and give you a kick up the arse.'

Though come to think of it I couldn't actually. She said, 'The paper's got a lot of money invested in you.' I said, 'Well, that's your funeral.'

Picture of him and the dog on the front page this morning, dog licking his face, ears up, paws on his shoulder, loving every minute of it. Spent the night in a hotel, five star, paid for by the newspaper. Article 'These nightmare months.' I stood by him, apparently. Says the longed-for reunion with his wife Marjory is scheduled for sometime this afternoon.

Police furious. The inspector in charge of the investigation said, 'Put it this way. We are not looking for anybody else.'

Sat waiting all afternoon. Photographers standing on the wall opposite, and on chairs and kitchen stools, two of them on top of a car. One up a tree. Police keeping the crowds back.

Getting dark when a big car draws up. Pandemonium.

Policeman bangs on the door, and Stuart's stood there on the doorstep and all the cameras going and them shouting, 'Stuart, Marjory. Over here. Over here please.' They want pictures of us with the dog, only the fellow from the newspaper says, No. They're going to be exclusive, apparently.

I said, 'Well, I've washed her kennel.' He says, 'She's not staying in there.' I said, 'You're not fetching her inside.' He said, 'I bloody am.' I said, 'Well, she'll have to stay on her paper.'

Later on when we're going to bed I wanted to shut her downstairs in the kitchen but he wouldn't have that either, keeps kissing her and whatnot and says she has to come upstairs.

When we're in bed he starts on straightaway and keeps asking Tina if she's taking it all in.

Afterwards he said, 'Are you surprised I'm not guilty?' I said, 'I'm surprised you got off.' He said, 'Don't you think I'm not guilty?' I said, 'I don't know, do I?' He said, 'You bloody do. You'd better bloody know. You're as bad as my mam.' I said, 'I'm not your mam.' He said, 'No, you're bloody not' and laughs.

I must have fallen asleep because when I wake up he's sleeping and the dog's off its paper, sat on his side of the bed watching him.

I get up and go downstairs and get the bin bag from under the stairs only I don't put any lights on. Then I get the poker and go out into the yard and push the slacks back under the kennel.

It's a bit moonlight and when I look over the gate they've all gone, just a broken chair on the pavement opposite.

I get back into bed and in a bit he wakes up and he has another go.

FADE.

NIGHTS IN
THE GARDENS OF SPAIN

ROSEMARY PENELOPE WILTON

Producer Mark Shivas *Director* Tristram Powell *Designer* Stuart Walker
Music George Fenton

A plain suburban drawing room wall. Rosemary is a middle-aged, middle-class woman, sitting on a chair.

Nobody normally gets killed round here; they're mostly detached houses and you never even hear shouting. So it took me a minute to tipple to what she was saying.

I said, 'Dead? Is it a heart attack?' She said, 'Oh no. Nothing like that. Just look at me, I'm in my bare feet.'

I really only know her to nod to but they have a lovely magnolia so once when she was in the garden I called out, 'You've had more luck with your magnolia grandiflora than I have.' But she just smiled and said, 'Yes.' And since I didn't have another remark up my sleeve ready, that was the end of that. I do that all the time, start a conversation but can't keep it going.

Blondish woman, a bit washed-out looking. Nice, tired sort of face. Anyway she comes out into the road and waits for me to get to their gate and says, 'I know I don't really know you, only there's something wrong with Mr McCorquodale.'

I was actually rushing because I'd planned on getting the five to nine and going into Sainsbury's but anyway I went in. I said, 'Has he been poorly?' She said, 'No. I've a feeling he's dead. Come through…only Mrs Horrocks…he doesn't have any trousers on.' I said, 'Well, I do a stint at the hospice twice a week, that's not a problem.' Only to be fair I just take the trolley round I've never actually been there when anybody's been going and they think I'm not really ready to administer the consolation yet.

She had a nice linen dress on, very simple. I think she might have been drinking.

He was lying on his back on the rug, one of those fleecy hairy things with blood and whatnot coming from somewhere behind his head. And it's awful because the first thing I thought was, Well, she'll never get that out.

He had on these green Y-fronty things which I'd have thought were a bit young for someone who's retired, but Henry's the same, suddenly takes it into his head to go in for something he thinks is a bit more dashing. Little Terylene socks. I said, 'Should I touch him?' She said, 'Well, you can if you want but he is dead. I've been sitting here looking at him for an hour.' I said, 'His pants are on back to front.' She said, 'Oh that's me. I thought I'd better put them on before I fetched somebody in.'

He had a little tattoo not far from his belly button and I remember when they moved in Henry said he thought he had something to do with vending machines.

I said, 'Did he bang his head, do you think?' She said, 'Oh no. I shot him. I've put the gun away.' And she opens the sideboard drawer and there it is with the tablemats and playing cards. He had a gun because he'd been in Malaya apparently.

My first thought was to ring Henry and ask what to do but I couldn't face the fuss. I was still a bit nervous of calling 999 because I'm never sure what constitutes an emergency. Anyway I thought if she'd waited an hour already I might as well get her a cup of tea first, and as I was running the tap I called out, 'The police haven't already been, have they?' She said, 'No. Why?' I said, 'Nothing.'

Only there was a pair of handcuffs on the draining board.

FADE.

Another wall.

The policeman had some difficulty writing. Big boy, nice ears, spelling all over the place.

When I asked him what he thought had happened he said, 'Well, it's marriage isn't it, the stresses and strains of. Though we don't normally expect it with oldish people, they've generally got it out of their system by then. And it's a bit early in the day. People seem to like to get breakfast out of the way before the shooting starts.'

I'm just signing my statement when Henry arrives back and of course prolongs the process. 'I don't know that Mrs Horrocks quite means this, officer. What you said to me on the phone, young lady was…' I said, 'Henry. You weren't there.' The policeman winks and says, 'Now then, we don't want another shooting match do we?'

I mean at first Henry didn't even know who they were. He said, 'Not the chow?' I said, 'No. That's the Broadbents.' Anyway he sits about for a bit, whistling under his breath, then goes upstairs and attacks his computer.

After the policeman had gone I went up and apologised and asked Henry whether he thought anything had been going on. He said, 'Why?' I said, 'Well, she didn't have anything on under that linen dress.' Of course any suggestion of that embarrasses Henry, he's such an innocent. He said, 'Rosemary, I don't know what sort of world you think you're living in but there's probably some perfectly reasonable explanation. In the meantime let's just remember that somebody has died. I'm only sorry that you had to be the one who was passing, because I'd have preferred you not to have been involved.'

I went out later to get some milk at the garage and there were still one or two reporters outside number 17, a whole branch of the magnolia broken off. One of them said, 'Are you a neighbour? Did you know the McCorquodales?' I shook my head and didn't say anything so one of them shouts after me, 'You owe it to the community.' So I turned round and said, 'Yes, and you owe it to the community not to break branches off people's magnolia trees.' And of course that's just the point where the photographer takes a picture and it's in the paper this morning with me looking like a mad woman and the caption 'The real face of suburbia.' Whereas the real face of suburbia was Henry's when he saw it.

I woke up in the night and I could hear him whistling under his breath. I said, 'Are you thinking about Mrs McCorquodale?' He said, 'No, I was thinking about the house. Prices are down as it is and something like this isn't going to help matters.' He reached over from his bed and took my hand. 'You must try not to be upset, but if we don't get at least 175 we shall have to kiss goodbye to Marbella.'

I keep wondering if I ought to have told somebody about the handcuffs.

FADE.

Rosemary is in the conservatory.

I'd put on my little greeny-coloured costume, which is at least tried and tested, only when I came down Henry said, 'Oh, are you going in that?' So I went and changed into the black. No need, because it was all very casual, the policeman in his shirt sleeves, and some barrister taking me through what I'd said, scarcely interested at all. I gave her a little smile; they let her sit down most of the time, she did look pale.

Pleaded not guilty, which you have to do apparently even when they know you did it, only then her lawyer reads out a list of stuff they'd found wrong with Mrs McCorquodale when she'd been arrested, old fractures, new cigarette burns and one of her teeth loose. Another lawyer then jumps up and said, 'Were other people involved?' And she said, 'No,' and he said he wouldn't pursue that at this stage. The upshot is she was sent for trial.

I said to Henry, 'Does that mean they'll have to go through it all
again?' He said, 'Oh yes. This is just the beginning.'

Policewoman came round this afternoon, said Did I want any
counselling? I'm entitled to it, apparently, through having seen a body
and should have had it earlier only they had a charabanc run off the
road so they've had a bit of a backlog.

Pleasant enough girl, though she would go on about all the terrible
dreadful things she'd seen, accidents and violence and whatnot, so my
seeing just one body seemed pretty ordinary really. But maybe that's part
of the counselling. We sat in the garden having some tea. Heavy on the
biscuits; polished off half a dozen sandwich creams. She said, It was nice
it was so civilised, had I seen a naked corpse before?

She was just going when she turns back and she says, 'Mrs Horrocks,
when I went on the counselling course one of the things they teach you
is that it helps to look things in the face right from the start.' I said,
'Well, I did look at the body; I actually touched it.' She said, 'Yes, but

when the police start digging, which they have to do, there is a potential for distress.' I said, 'Digging?' She said, 'Metaphorically.' I said, 'Why should it affect me?' She said, 'All the indications are that it won't. But the potential is there. Things come out and I want you to know I'm here for you. I'm on a bleep.'

I said to Henry, 'It's nice she should be so concerned.' He said, 'It's what she's there for…unfortunately.'

Article in the *Mail* yesterday, which I'd always thought was that bit more refined but it's full of silly stuff about the case, what goes on behind the neat privet hedges-type-thing. I said to Henry, Fat lot they know. There actually isn't a privet hedge in the entire road. They're mostly beech and one or two cypresses leylandii. He said he didn't think that was quite the point and to a reporter a hedge was simply something to be peered through.

Still, talking of neat, what with her being away on remand their garden which is usually so immaculate is already beginning to look a bit… well…shaggy. She's got a herb garden outside the back door and the borage has gone berserk, bullying its way all over the border. Made me long to nip over and put it in its place.

I didn't want to ask Henry, though, as I was sure he'd think it 'Inadvisable, Rosemary, quite candidly,' but no, it turns out he's all in favour and it had in fact occurred to him, though, it has to be said, coming at it from a different angle from me, saying that if ever we're going to get anywhere near our asking price a garden going to seed in the same road is the last thing one wants.

So the upshot is I've started toddling up the road with my trusty secateurs. Thought I'd cut back the poppies now that they've flowered and give the achillea a chance to come through. Of course, I've scarcely got my kneeling pad down before Miss Lumsden's out, contriving to come by with an unconvincing bottle of Lucozade en route for the bottle bank. Wants to know if there are any sweet peas going begging. I said I'd thought of picking some and taking them down to the hospice. She said 'What a nice idea. Some people might feel a bit funny about them but I suppose they're too far gone to care.'

And lots of jokes of course. On the lines of Mr Pemberton's 'Who do I have to shoot for you to come and do my garden?' Smile got a bit fixed after a bit. Except that Sheila Blanchard did actually come in and lend a hand weeding the borders. Said she didn't blame her a bit. 'I mean husbands, Rosemary. Who needs them?' I said, 'Well, they can be a comfort.' She said, 'Can they? Reggie isn't. I'm the comfort merchant.

What's Henry like?' 'Oh,' I said 'very…' and I said such a silly word 'very considerate.' I saw her smile and she's a nice woman but I know it'll be all up and down the road by tomorrow.

But he is considerate. Timid, I suppose. Always has been. Wish he wasn't sometimes.

What I haven't told Henry is that I dropped Mrs McCorquodale a note to the prison, bringing her up to date on what I've been doing. I do it every day now, in fact, even send her snaps. Told her today I was keeping an eye on the alchemilla mollis, lovely plant but you have to read it the riot act occasionally.

She rang this afternoon to thank me. I didn't know you could do that in prison, ring up. Her name's Fran.

'Dear Fran…'

FADE.

The conservatory.

I've misjudged Henry. Got him quite wrong. Thirty years of marriage and you think you've got somebody all weighed up but no. He's lost half a stone while the case has been going on – and never set foot in the office. I thought, well, you're a better person than ever I thought you were. I said to Fran, 'He's more worried about you than he's ever been about me.' I mean the day I had my scan he went off to a golf tournament.

So as a reward I got out the brochures for Marbella and that seemed to cheer him up.

It's all come out in court, though. Turns out that Mr has led her a dog's life. Literally. The defence produced the collar and lead in evidence. Beat her. Terrorised her. 'A saga of protracted and imaginative cruelty' counsel said.

The prosecution, of course, goes after her, claiming it was all part of some game, sexually speaking, and that the cruelty was what she wanted. But she said if it had been mutual he wouldn't have been interested. Anyway how is it mutual to have your arm broken?

A lot of lurid details, how he sometimes used to put a hood over her head so's she couldn't see and bring in other people to watch. Business associates, she thought. Leading lights in the world of vending machines, probably.

Henry says she was lucky because there was another case going on the same week up in Liverpool, a man had up for killing a child, and that pushed her out of the limelight a bit.

Of course, what Henry calls the wild and woolly feminist ladies were out in force even shouting from the gallery. 'To a degree irresponsible,' Henry said. 'However mitigating the circumstances, Rosemary, she has to be looking at a custodial sentence.' Then, when he only gave her two years, the judge gets it in the neck from the law and order brigade. But, as Sheila Blanchard said, 'Worth every minute of it, dear, if you ask me. A couple of years basket weaving and you get the bed to yourself. Cheap at the price. I just wish I had a gun. As it is I'm pinning my hopes on his prostate.'

I can't go and see her so often now she's convicted and Henry doesn't know I go at all. Well, I've never had a best friend, the sort you can tell everything to. Never had one, never been one, even when I was a girl. Not the type, I suppose. And no secrets to tell either. And with not having children I wasn't a member of that club either.

She's in Rissington, the other side of York. It's one of these modern places, looks like a business park or an out of town shopping centre. Crimes 'R' Us. She's transformed the prison garden, which used to be very utilitarian, cabbages, lettuces and whatnot.

Only now she's got them to do some interplanting, even make it a bit of a potager…and while it's never going to be Sissinghurst…the site's too windy…it's still streets ahead of what it was. She has visions of it being open to the public but that's difficult with it being a prison. We go and sit on a seat in the garden and she's started telling me about all the stuff he forced her to do. Said she wanted me to know in case it made me not want to see her any more. I said, 'Don't be silly.' But terrible things I never knew people did. And with the hood over her head and men there, watching in silence. More than watching actually.

One of them who had a funny habit…and I knew what she was going to say the second before she said it…a funny habit of whistling under his breath.

Pause.

Of course, a lot of people do that.

FADE.

Kitchen.

'I see they're selling the Murder House,' Sheila Blanchard calls out to me this morning. 'The board's gone up. Asking 160.' I didn't say I knew, or that actually it's sold already. Fran says they're an Asian family, quite well-to-do, have a chain of electrical shops. I thought, Well, that won't do Marbella any good. Poor Henry. Golf with Jimmy Tarbuck takes a knock.

I look at him a lot now, this once upon a time spectator, or maybe still, who knows, somewhere. And I think...Well, sometimes I just think, 'You dark horse.' Other times I think about Fran and get upset. He caught me staring at him the other night, said 'What are you looking at, young lady?' I said, predictably, 'Nothing.' 'You've been getting a bit broody lately,' he said. And he patted me on the knee. *(She pulls a face.)*

What I'd actually been thinking was whether all these years he'd been wanting to see me crawl round the room naked on my hands and knees. No worse than bedding out, I suppose, though if I did it nowadays I'd have to have my knee pads on, which might take the edge off things a bit.

But I think about the collar and lead, then I think Well, that's what my marriage has been like too, being jerked along. I mean, what else is Marbella?

We never settled on what to call it, that was part of the trouble. The garden's made me quite used to things having a common name and a Latin one. Only with sex neither seemed to suit Henry. Coming from me, anyway. Just got embarrassed.

He's no idea I go and see her. I tell him it's the hospice. The farm goes from strength to strength; she's put her onions in for shows and gone commercial with the tomatoes. She's there every free moment, well, I say free. Except that when I say goodbye at the gate it feels it's me that's going back to prison.

Once a month they let her out for a half day and we go off for the afternoon and do all sorts. Open gardens, obviously, auctions we've been to, car boot sales. And old churches, which I've never cared much for, only Fran knows a lot about them. One church in the middle of a field near where there'd been a battle. And we sit there in a pew while she explains all the architectural features. And sometimes I think I've never been so happy in my life.

She took my arm this last time, just as we were coming down some steps at Fountains Abbey and then, when we got to the bottom, she didn't let go. It was just like it was when I was a girl when a boy did it. Such a bold step. And so meant.

And I thought, here I am strolling arm in arm with someone who murdered her husband. I said...out loud...'I know what this is.' She said, 'What is it?' I said, 'It's life.'

She wasn't feeling all that clever today so we just went and sat in the grounds, and she held my hand again. Going into York next week for a check-up. I thought I could go along and hang about the hospital just on the off-chance I might see her but she'll be with a warder apparently so I won't.

Gave me this.

She has a large tomato which she puts to her cheek.

FADE.

A patio wall. A tropical night. Crickets, etc.

I've never had to start a garden from scratch before. There are no features at all. Flat, square, stony it's like one of the 'before' pictures in the gardening magazines. Or an exercise yard.

A lawn's pretty much out of the question in this heat and the water supply's very quixotic, though Henry says the greens at the golf club are immaculate. And he saw Sean Connery last week. So I sit and look at it and draw plans. 'Look on it as a challenge,' Henry says. 'You'll crack it, young lady' he says. 'I know you.' *(The dialogue is now quite broken up.)*

She died, did Fran. A lot of toing and froing before they eventually tracked it down. No surprise to either of us. Doctors. It's the first thing that occurs to you and the last thing that occurs to them. By which time it's too late. 'Oh, it was always too late, Mrs Horrocks.'

She was in a hospice at the finish so I knew the drill. I used to hold her hand, kiss it. And she'd kiss mine. We'd talked about a little garden centre.

Best thing that could have happened, Henry said. Which is when I should have packed my bags. Instead of which I just went and sat in the greenhouse for a bit. Typical.

He'll sometimes wear one of these caps with the big peaks that boys wear. Reckons it's for the sun. Caught him the other day wearing it back to front. I suppose it's known as a new lease of life.

There are supposed to be lots of criminals round here. Bank robbers and such like who can't go back, play golf all day.

Of course it's just what would happen in a play. Fran shot him so she had to pay. Only this place is crawling with people who haven't paid. Unless you count just being here as paying.

The gardening books talk about the plants that are supposed to like shade. They say they prefer it.

I don't believe it. I don't believe anything likes shade. They do perfectly well in the shade, it's true. But give them even...*(and there's quite a long pause)* give them a bit of sun and suddenly they come into their own.

I sit here at night, listening to the frogs and the crickets, and Henry, whistling under his breath.

FADE.

WAITING FOR THE TELEGRAM

VIOLET THORA HIRD

Producer Mark Shivas *Director* Stuart Burge *Designer* Stuart Walker
Music George Fenton

The speaker is an old lady in a wheelchair. She has a rug over her knees. The background is plain and uncluttered. Sometimes she is parked by a radiator, sometimes by a window or the end of a bed. The shots need not be continuous as written but can be broken up by a cutaway of Violet's hands, twisting her handkerchief, turning her wedding-ring or just folded in her lap. Sometimes when she is trying to remember things or express them she fills up with tears but these are only brief and she generally battles on.

I saw this feller's what-do-you-call-it today. Except I'm not supposed to say 'what-do-you-call-it'. Verity says, 'Violet. What-do-you-call-it is banned. When we cannot find the word we want we *describe*, we do not say 'what-do-you-call-it'. Well, you won't catch me describing that. Besides, 'what-do-you-call-it' *is* what I call it. Somebody's what-do-you-call-it. Anyway I saw it.

I didn't think anything about it only somebody must have gone and alerted the office because next thing you know Bouncing Betty poles in. She says, 'Violet, I have to ask you this. Was the penis erect?' I said, 'Nurse Bapty. That's not a word I would use.' She said, 'Erect?' I said, 'No. The other.' She said, 'Well, Violet. You've had what we call a stroke. You're sometimes funny with words.' I said, 'I'm not funny with that word.' She said, 'Things have changed now, Violet. Penis is its name. All the other names are just trying to make it more acceptable. Language is a weapon, Violet. We're at war.' I said, 'Who with?' She said, 'Men.'

He was a smartish feller, can't have been more than seventy and a lovely blue suit. He could have been a bank manager except he had no socks on. I said, 'You can put that away.' He said, 'I've got a big detached house in Harrogate.' I said, 'That's no excuse.' He said, 'It's got five bathrooms.'

She turns her wheelchair.

They've inaugurated this what-do-you-call *(She checks herself)*…this chair-lift thing. I think he must have come up from downstairs. There's been one or two of them trying to migrate. They get bored. Do you wonder? Anyway when he saw it wasn't cutting much ice with me he takes it over to Hilda, only she's busy braying on her tray with her spoon so it doesn't make much of an impact there either. Mary's asleep and when he wakes her up and says, 'Look at this', she says, 'Is it dinner-time?' and goes back to sleep again.

In the finish he comes back to me and says, 'I've forgotten, did

I show you this?' At which point Rene rushes in, sees his lordship with
his trousers down and says, 'Are you my taxi? I'm all ready.'

I said to Francis, 'And they call it a rest home.'

FADE.

They haven't given it up. We were throwing this ball about…a big, felty
thing…I could never catch a ball when I was little so I know I can't do it
now. Anyway Nurse Bapty comes in and wheels me to the window and
says, 'Violet, having seen this penis, would you like some counselling?'
I said, 'Nurse. I'm nearly 95.' She said, 'Yes, Violet, but you're a victim
and choose how old you are, you're still flying the flag of gender.' I said,
'Well I think a cup of tea would do the trick, Nurse Bapty, thank you.'
I call them all Nurse and she is a nurse only a lot of them aren't, they're
just young lasses.

Francis is a proper nurse, though, he's got letters after his name and
you can tell because he has me out of my clothes in no time. I said,
'Somebody tried to undress me once, only he wasn't a patch on you.
Are you as sharp as this with your girl friend?' He said, 'You're my girl
friend.'

He has some grand arms.

FADE.

I can't reckon up names. New lass on this afternoon, bonny little thing,
helping Francis put me to bed for my lie down. I said, 'What's your
name, love?' She says, 'Devon.' I says, 'That's never a name, it's a place.'
She says, 'Yes, a very beautiful place. My mam and dad used to go on
holiday there.' I said, 'Well, it's a good job they didn't go to Skegness.'

She looks right mad, only Francis laughs so she laughs an' all. I think
she's got her eye on him.

I drop off and when I wake up there's a fellow by my bed. He goes,
'Hello!' I said, 'Hello' and shut my eyes again. They send these folks
round to test you.

When I open them again he's still there. 'Hello!,' he goes. Fattish feller,
sixty odd, gingery tash. He said, 'It's Donald, mother. I'm your son.'

He didn't look like a son, looked more like a father. Big wristwatch,
attaché case, one of these green raincoaty-things they shoot in. Anyway
I take no notice and he starts on the Hello! game again. Hello! Hello!
Made me feel like a budgie. I said, 'Bugger off.'

Mrs…Mrs…light-coloured lady…Shah comes in, starts squeegeeing round. He says, 'It's tragic, isn't it. She'd never had a day's illness in her life. I think it's a disease of civilisation. Does it happen in your country?' She says, 'I'm from Huddersfield.'

Then Rene comes in, ready for off as usual. She says, 'Are you my taxi? I've been waiting all morning.' 'I've just remembered,' he says, 'I'm wanted in Wakefield,' shoves his tash in my face and he's off. Mrs Shah says, 'Was that your son?' I said, 'He thinks so.' She says, 'My son's got in to do engineering. He's six foot two.'

I lay there working it out. If I had a son I must have had a…husband. So when Francis was wiping my bottom later on I said, 'Did I get married?' He said, 'Yes, can't you remember?' I said, 'I remember one young man but I don't think I took the plunge. Are you married?' He said, 'You get star treatment here, Violet. Even the Queen doesn't get her bottom wiped.'

FADE.

What's her name came round today…her that helps me with talking…*(She thinks)*…name of a cricket bat, else a gas oven…Verity. She's a nice-looking lass but makes nowt of herself, a big jumper thing…I said, I bet you've got a right nice…' She goes, 'Describe, Violet, describe…' I said, 'A right nice…them two things with pink ends that men like…Bust.'

By, she did look narked! She said, 'Things are different now, Violet. Women have control of their own bodies.' I said, 'Is that why I can't get them to take me to the toilet?'

Then we start doing these exercises, naming folks. I'm quite good at that…Rene, Mary, Hilda. And then I get stuck. She says, 'Describe, Violet. Say, the lady in the yellow frock.' I said, 'The black lady.' She said, 'No, Violet. It's better to say the lady in the yellow frock.'

I says to Francis, 'It's a complicated business talking. I never used to give it a thought.' He said, 'What?'

He wasn't listening. He was miles away. Really quiet. Not like him. He's generally so full of…them things you get in tins…beans!

He's a lovely looking lad.

FADE.

Rene gollops her food. She was sick today all down Francis's front.
I said, 'You gollop your food, you.' She said, 'Well, I have to. I've got a
taxi coming.' I said, 'Rene, where's this taxi taking you?' She said,
'Armley.' I said, 'Armley where?' She said, 'My mam and dad's in 1947.'
I said, 'Well, if he can take you there I bet he does a spanking trade.'

Anyway she fetches her dinner back all down Francis. So he says,
'You'll have to excuse me, ladies' and he takes his...tunicky thing...right
off. And by, he's a grand-looking lad! Not a mark on him and right big
(She mimes shoulders)...here. It made you want to...*(She mimes a
kiss)*...do that, whatever it's called. Lovely. Devon came in I saw her
having a look.

When he's finished cleaning up he says, 'Well, Violet you've seen
something today.' I said, 'I've seen it before.' He just has a little bit of
this *(She touches her hair)*...starting here *(She touches her chest)*. Like they
do at that age. *(She starts to cry)* I said, 'Don't go get yourself...' He said,
'What?' I said, 'Like when you don't come back. Khaki...poppies.'

He said, 'Nay, that's all done with now. They don't die like that.' And he looked right...*(She touches her cheeks meaning tears)*...what's it called?

FADE.

I saw my legs today. I didn't own them. They didn't look like my legs at all. That Devon was giving me a bath. I said, 'Them's never my legs.' She said, 'Whose legs do you think they are?' I said, 'Well, you never know in this place. I've had somebody else's teeth before now. And this frock isn't mine. Tangerine doesn't suit me. Where's that green little frock?' She said, 'Hilda kept wetting herself in it and it's gone funny.' Francis wouldn't have put me in this frock. Only he wasn't there.

She's putting me back on the bed and I said, 'Well I've learned one thing. I'm not Betty Grable.' She says, 'Who's she?' No wonder your talking goes...even when you get it right they think you're barmy. Francis knows all the old film stars...Betty Grable...her that sings and that one with the cig and her hair up...bit of a madam...Bette Davis.

Anyway I'm sitting up in bed when they all waltz in with this cake. Turns out it's my birthday. I'm ninety something...I don't know, they did tell me. Candles. Tasted like candles did the cake. Anyway I had to reckon to be...pleased *(She pretends to smile)*...Kept saying a few years more and I'll be getting the...now then...lad comes on a bike...folks stood at the door, weeping...telegram. Her on the horse at the end of the pictures, she sends it you apparently. Queen.

No Francis though. I said to Nurse Bapty, 'Where is he?' She said, 'He's gone for a check-up.' I said, 'Check-up for what?' She said, 'Oh, they do that now.'

Pause.

I hate tangerine.

FADE.

Verity fetches a young lad in this morning. She says to him, 'You're privileged. Violet is our oldest resident.' She says, 'Spencer's going to ask you one or two questions for his school project. It's about the past.'

Poor-looking lad, bonny face. Floppy clothes, shirt-tail out. I said, 'Is that your big brother's jumper?' He says, 'No. It's dead smart is this.' Gets out his exercise book, and says, 'What was it like then?' I said,

'Well…' He said, 'Were things better or worse?' I said, 'Well, my legs were better.' He said he didn't mean that. Verity comes back and he says, 'She doesn't seem to know what I'm talking about.' Verity says, 'Well, she's had a stroke. Come on, I'll find you another one.' *(Violet is a bit upset.)*

I said to Francis, 'He'd mean trams and whatnot. Strikes. Tin-baths. The war.' Francis says, 'Which war?' I said, 'The proper war when all the young lads got killed. "Never again." That war.' He looked right sad and he said, 'Hold my hand.' So I did. Then he said, 'Did you have a young man?' I said, 'Yes.' He said, 'What was he like?' I said, 'His name was Edward. They had a little confectioner's down Tong Road. He used to fetch my mam a vanilla slice. Every time he came round, a vanilla slice.'

I still had hold of his hand. I said, 'When you were courting then, it was a kind of…where you fight…' He said, 'Struggle.' I said, 'Ay. He'd manage to get one button undone one night, and another the next. And lasses weren't supposed to do much in them days, just lie back and get ready to draw the line. And because I'd let him get so far one night, he'd know where the front line was, so the next night he'd get there a bit quicker and push on a bit further…another button, you know. It was that…grudging somehow. But it was the way you felt you had to be then.

Anyway he was going off to France next day; he was in camp over at Church Fenton and they'd given him a pass for his last night. My mam…oh she was a good 'un…she put some anemones in a vase… I love anemones…and put a fire in the front room and then she reckoned she had to stay at my Aunt Florence's that night. Ordinary folks then were better than they're ever given credit for, for all they were so straitlaced.

I gave him his tea and then we went and sat in the front room and he started on like, undoing my buttons and kissing and whatnot. Only I'd wanted to look nice so I'd put on my best frock and he couldn't fathom how it unfastened. I should just have taken it off but I didn't and, poor lamb, he got so fed up with these flaming buttons, in the finish he gave up.

He'd taken his leggings…his puttees off…because they were hot and he was in his shirtsleeves; they were right rough khaki shirts then, really cheap and itchy. Anyway in the finish he gets up off the sofa and says, "Hang this lot," and he takes his shirt off and everything else besides. Doesn't say a word, just takes it all off and stands there on the hearthrug. Oh and he looked a picture, with the fire and that. Not a mark on him. Then he says, "Take your clothes off now."

She covers her face with her hands.

And I didn't. I didn't. And I wanted him so much. I don't know…it was just the way I'd been brought up. And he stands there looking down at me…and then he just picks his clothes up and goes next door and after a bit I heard the front door bang.

They look old in photographs compared with what they look now. Only they weren't. They were lads, same as you. And just as grand.

Pause.

I saw the yellow thing the boy on the bike brings…his sister fetches it round…telegram. And a vanilla slice for mam. Then later on they had a letter reckoning to be from the King, same as everybody did who'd lost somebody. They keep saying I'll be getting a telegram soon…for my birthday.'

Francis says, 'Do you know something Violet? In all that, you never said, "What do you call it," or "What's its name." Not once. You knew all the words.'

'Only I should have let him, shouldn't I? I've never forgiven myself.'

'Well,' Francis says, 'how can you know?' Still holding my hand.

Pause.

Poor lad, he looks right washed out.

FADE.

I thought they'd got pneumonia beat. A big strapping lad like Francis. Devon said it was a blessing, he'd have died anyway. I said, 'A blessing? A young feller like that?'

And he was such a gentle soul. She was doing my legs, plastering me up with stuff and right hard hands, not a patch on Francis. I said, 'He'd have made some lass a grand husband.' She said, 'It wasn't lasses; it was lads.' I said, I knew it was lads. She said, 'Well I wish you'd told me.' Right nasty.

Pause.

I didn't know it was lads but I wasn't having her telling me. Lads or lasses, he was a love.

Rene's gone an' all.

Violet looks towards the empty bed.

Went in the night. They thought I was asleep so they didn't bother to put the screens round. Saw it all. Putting the white socks on. Bit of giggling. Right as rain when she came to bed. Made me promise to wake her up if her taxi came. Well, it came in the finish. I said to Francis…no, I didn't.

Pause.

My arm seems to have gone to sleep this morning and this hand.

She looks at her hand.

Now then I'll have another one of these somewhere.

She locates her other hand, lifts it onto her lap and sits with her hands folded. She sings.

I've got sixpence
Jolly jolly sixpence
I've got sixpence
To last me all my life
I've got twopence to spend
And twopence to lend
And twopence to send home to my wife.

If we sang everything I shouldn't forget.

All this very broken up with pauses.

Pets is what you want in this place. Else babies. Summat you can… *(She makes a stroking movement)* do this with. Not have to talk to.

Pause.

It's no game is this.

Pause.

We're the pets. Fed and cleaned out every day. It's a kennels is this.

Pause.

Pedigree Chum. Pedigree Chum.

FADE.

THE ALAN BENNETT COLLECTION

Also available from BBC Worldwide

Audio:
Talking Heads 2 (cassette and CD)
Talking Heads (cassette and CD)
Talking Heads Book and Audio pack
Alan Bennett Boxed Set: contains *Diaries* and *The Lady in the Van*
Alan Bennett Double Bill: Forty Years On and *A Woman of No Importance*
The Lady in the Van and *Uncle Clarence*
Poetry in Motion
The Alan Bennett Diaries 1980–1990 (cassette and CD)
The Clothes They Stood Up In
Alan Bennett at the BBC

Video:
Talking Heads

Books:
Talking Heads
The Complete Talking Heads